# THE BRIDPORT PRIZE

## POETRY, SHORT STORIES AND

C000213288

## JUDGES
Kirsty Logan • Short Stories and Flash Fiction
Hollie McNish • Poetry

redcliffe

First published in 2019 by Redcliffe Press Ltd
81g Pembroke Road, Bristol BS8 3EA

e: info@redcliffepress.co.uk
www.redcliffepress.co.uk
Follow us on Twitter @RedcliffePress

© the contributors

Follow The Bridport Prize:
Follow us on Twitter @BridportPrize
www.bridportprize.org.uk
www.facebook.com/bridportprize

ISBN 978-1-911408-59-8

British Library Cataloguing-in-Publication Data
A catalogue record for this book is available from the British Library

All rights reserved. Except for the purpose of review, no part of this
book may be reproduced, stored in a retrieval system, or transmitted, in
any form or by any means, electronic, mechanical, photocopying,
recording or otherwise, without the prior permission of the publishers.

Typeset in 10.5pt Times

Typeset by Addison Print Ltd, Northampton
Printed by Hobbs the Printers Ltd, Totton

# Contents

HOLLIE McNISH

# Poetry Report

I'll start by making the obvious point that any decision in poetry compe-
titions will always be subjective. Another judge may have chosen other
winners and no doubt people will disagree with some of my choices.

Personally, when judging poetry, I look for form and for feeling and for
the imprint that the writing makes upon my internal organs as it repeats
on me (in both positive and negative ways) post-reading. My personal
preference in poetry is a clean shaped page of words. That said, if writing
is too visceral to fit into such neatly trimmed linguistics, so be it.

In the thirteen poems I chose, I found something of all my poetic joys,
with my final three balancing a content which whipped my guts, locked
my tongue up or split my lips into grins, but which still cut a structure and
vocabulary suited expertly.

The ten highly commended winners were perhaps the hardest to
choose, such was the variety amongst the submissions.

First, 'Art History'. The moment I read this delicate poem, I was
meddling in Hokusai's studio. Such little embellishment, but still an entire
scene immediately unravelled. I laughed, learnt and nodded, yes, to the
genius of ridiculousness. An utterly enticing poem.

'Equity' gutted me. Some stand out sharpness – *She's young for there /
There are no visitors,* plus the continuing play on the open / un-curtained
windows. The final line of this poem was perhaps my favourite of all. I
was heart broken.

'Seeds', shaped lovingly into the title's oval form, was a surprise love.
I often find shape poems forced or unfitting, but here the voracious, fierce
nature of the content clung in marvellous picturesque contrast.

'Big Jim' I did not notice much on first reading. Once on a break,
however, I realised I was still thinking of him. By second and third
reading, I was praising, rather than ignoring, the more monosyllabic
patterning, and the images such as kids 'like scattered thistledown' or
chopping wood 'as if...cutting into chunks his wife's old boyfriends'
stuck. I went back for several peaks at Jim kissing through the final
window. I am a soppy pervert perhaps.

'Ghost Apples' sent shivers as instant pictures appeared; so vivid, this

5

tragic metaphor, placed brilliantly, simply yet stridently, on the page, the sharp twist between winter fields and grief a horrific comfort to cling to.

'Tinder Box' was so full, so verbose in its approach to tragedy. I praised the specifics of this poem; the giant orange poppy fireballs, the burning sagebrush, the chaparral. I felt that everything was noticed and recorded; superb snapshots of sound and sight, panic and loss.

'Gameplay' sent giggles bursting forth. The italics in this poem – *so long* shifting rocks – floored me. A marvellous comic selection of the most obscure of gaming references mixed with a wink and a jab at the uselessness of human onlookers. The comedy of cruel futility.

The surreal nature of 'Assembling God' had me picking it apart for weeks; the rubix cube of the collection perhaps. It was a challenging poem for me, but a greatly enticing challenge and sometimes that is what I want in a reading.

'The Way You Knew' I fell for when reading it aloud. I felt the rhythms, repetitions and internal rhymes slipped so subtly between pauses came forth more confidently when leashed from tongue, whilst images such as 'the way you knew as you chewed how big the next bubble would be' and 'even before he began drinking ink' ensured it would not slip into generalisation.

Finally, for those highly commended, 'Epiphany'. It was the momentary and mindful nature of this poem that I adored: the flitting strands of thought, the continual physical movement throughout, the humour in the mix of everyday and universal. And then the ending, I loved the ending. I saw the tulip.

Though my top three were chosen early on, their order was not, but I finally settled.

'Three Candles' is my third place. I dare to say I will never forget this poem. Such stripped down dialogue – a tragic 'chat'. The poem explained nothing, showed everything. The lines 'And I give him a look / And he shuts up' are piercing to me in this respect. I loved the breathlessness of opening mid-scene, the frightful repetitions, the staccato structure of this fight to remember and to honour and to come to terms with.

'Hoor', my second place, I read and re-read for days. On each re-read, I discovered new patterns, new tangos of words dancing into the spotlight. I really enjoy writing that blasts chatter into ears. I love hearing tongues waggle. Here, I was the invisible fly in the field, eavesdropping, giggling, tearing up at the final first kiss. I also cannot stop repeating the line: the tax man, a *connivin little hoors bollix* in my head, but that's by the by.

My winner was THINGS I WISH I COULD TRADE MY HEADSCARF FOR.

I read and hear many poems about prejudice – they are often the staple of a spoken word poetry scene and whilst the subjects they raise are always, unfortunately, needed, welcomed, vital, it was the originality and imagination within this poem which deemed it my final favourite.

I found this poem both superbly childish and wretchedly mature: the scarf speaking parseltongue to waiting bigots; the opening list of abstract, playful, yet terrible comparisons; a tempo, which, added to some of the almost tongue-twisting expressions, kept my breath held throughout. For me, this poem represented one of the neatest examples of the contrast between the enthusiasm and imagination of a young mind and the prejudices it ought never to have had used these for.

I could write so much more here, but I'll finish with a thank you to the authors instead. What a pleasure it was to be allowed in.

To those of you about to peruse this anthology, I hope you enjoy reading these poems as much as I hated having to choose between them.

# Short Story Report

Reading the stories for the Bridport Prize 2019 was not only an honour, but also a pleasure. My favourite thing about having the chance to read so many different voices at once was the way the stories seem to speak to one another. One story told of a small girl pretending to be a wolf pup; the next of a group of mysterious part-wolf, part-woman creatures taking revenge on violent men. One story explored the complex moral and emotional conflicts of a man emigrating to an unfamiliar country; the next laid out the complex moral and emotional conflicts of a worker at an immigrant detainment centre. It was a pleasure to imagine the stories in dialogue: the wolf-girl grown into a wolf-woman, the flipped coin of the immigration experience.

Clear themes emerged as I read on. Infidelity, divorce and grief centred many of the stories, often from the perspective of a child. Marriages and relationships were generally failed or failing; love was unrequited; babies much hoped for were lost or never begun. From this I take that there are lots of writers out there going through difficult times, perhaps using fiction as a life raft. This is something I can certainly identify with, and it's reassuring to see that stories can have many functions.

'Bedded' by Mikaella Clements is a steady-paced piece of perfection – confidently told, and creating a strange and beautiful world. It's a tender and knowing piece of storytelling.

Nici West's 'Crow' haunted me in the best possible way; its sinister imagery and body horror comes together in an emotional and satisfying ending. It's a story that stayed with me for a long time after I'd read it.

The raw, heartbreaking brutality of 'Fermented' by Gemma Reeves isn't something I come across every day, and when I do get to read it, I can't help but be impressed. The command of language, slow build of tension and refusal to shy away from the inevitable ending is a joy to read.

It's not easy to pull off second-person narration, but Hesse Phillips 'The Way of the Pack' achieves it. I thought there were no new ways under the sun to explore a parent's fears for (and sometimes of) their child, but I was wrong; here the emotional honesty rings true.

Not one, but two impressive feats of second-person narration:

Joseph Boone's 'The Sound of Water' is raw, tragic, sensual and packed full of beautifully-wrought description.

'Exactly the Thing That You Are' by Jane Flett was such a joy to read – the exploration of a much-maligned form of performance and athletic skill, told with such precision and compassion.

With 'Wolf Women', Amy Stewart masterfully takes us from the sinister opening line to an ending that feels both chilling and satisfying – not an easy thing to achieve, but here it's incredibly well done.

Alissa Jones Nelson's 'Al-Watan' took me on an incredible journey – not just geographically with the protagonist, but emotionally as I weathered the storms of his experience. It's a beautiful and unflinching piece of work.

With 'I Shouldn't Be Calling This Late', Jenny Karlsson casts a spell with words: the prose is such a pleasure to read, and displays an incredible command over language. It's a subtle story with many layers of hidden depth.

Jimmy Lowther's 'Salva Nos' raises a fascinating multitude of questions. The joy was reading on to see how those questions would be explored and how the atmosphere and creeping sense of unease would resolve.

It was no easy task to choose three winners from the impressive pool of submitted stories, but there was no denying the power of these pieces even among the other stories I loved. Anna Metcalfe's 'Start Again' pulled off no mean feat: it created a fictional world that wasn't pleasant to be in, but that I wanted to return to, just to know these characters better and immerse myself more in the prose.

When thinking of Sulaxana Hippisley's 'The Quarter Loaf' I'm surprised to remember that these aren't real people I can go and speak to; they feel solid, tangible, and the love and loneliness in their lives rings true.

Ross Foster's 'Henry' is smart, tender and brutal, with an ending that made me gasp out loud. The moment that elevates the story from a good story to something very special is when the protagonist goes into the kitchen and picks up the knife: her rush of blood, her intention.

If there's anything I want to say when signing off here, it's this: keep going. Keep writing. Keep dreaming and thinking and observing. I read an incredible variety of voices and worlds and histories in these stories, and I know there are so many more stories out there still to be written. So please: write them.

# Flash Fiction Report

Judging the flash fiction category was a particular joy for me, as I'm a huge fan of flash fiction – both reading it and writing it. It's an under-appreciated form of fiction, and I applaud every writer who approached this tricky type of storytelling. It's not easy to tell a complete, satisfying story with such a tiny word count; the fact that so many stories were submitted in this category is a testament to the skills of the writers out there.

I won't lie: when the stack of stories arrived through my letterbox, I was intimidated. How to read so many stories and judge them, one against another? Isn't it comparing apples and oranges? Observation that rings true as struck glass vs. glorious flights of imagination? A wide-ranging world vs. a perfectly-described miniature? Lyrical prose vs. a pacy plot? Which is 'better'? Is there such a thing as 'best'? But when it came down to it, choosing the winners was simple. I chose the stories that wouldn't leave. The ones I narrated to my wife, the ones I thought about while falling asleep, the ones I kept returning to. The ones that burrowed in.

'Ligature' by Daniel Bennett was one such story; I couldn't stop thinking about it after I read it. While the details may initially seem mundane, it's precisely the everyday nature of them that gives the story its power, right to the double-meaning of the heartrending last line.

Louise Cato's 'Small Bones' is a master-class in imagery and description. The beetroot, the pig-skin, the still-warm mice: while reading I can almost feel them and taste them.

'Genocide Memorial Week, Rwanda 2019' by Isabella Mead pulls off a wonderful feat of ambiguous intent, using a small but significant event to convey a profound and affecting story.

And on to the winners, all of which have achieved something very impressive – creating entire worlds, strong characters and intense backstories out of a lean, mean amount of words. These pieces are that rare thing: stories that may be tiny in word-count, but feel huge in implication. They are a keyhole we can peep through to see an entire world.

'Vigil' by Amanda O'Callaghan was one of the smallest stories in terms of word count, but packs an incredible punch. It's a testament to the fact that in the hands of a talented writer, only a few words are needed to convey a huge story with real emotional impact.

What I loved about Mike Kilgannon's 'The Hercules Reopened' was the ambiguity, expertly balanced to create a multitude of possible interpretations. Every time I read the story I come up with something new, and the rhythms of the prose are a joy each time.

Maria Donovan's 'Aftermath' leapt out immediately: it's a masterclass in flash fiction, cramming more character development and world-building into 250 words than some writers manage in a whole novel. It's a truly impressive piece of writing.

To all the winners: congratulations, and I can't wait to read more of your work. To every writer who submitted a flash fiction this year: well done on writing this wonderful and unappreciated form. And to every writer out there who thought about submitting, but didn't: keep writing!

FATHIMA ZAHRA

# Things I Wish I Could Trade My Headscarf For

A fishbowl/ a space helmet/a tin foil hat/ bubble wrap/ a shoe box/ a
handful of snakes/ and it will still be the least suspicious thing in a train
carriage/ this country sings of all the ways it loves us/ in the soft slip of
hate mail through our front door/ how eyes under furrowed brows walk
me down the aisle in tube carriages/ how men flip us off as my dad
drives me to the train station/ how a face peers out window rolled down
to scream/ MUZLIM! / and I think, yes? / I am? / my scarf speaks
parseltongue now/ eggs spectators on as if to say/ 'here is an empty
goalpost/ kick those slurs in' / my parents hold their breath / don't let
out/ till I walk back in again/this is no way to live/ between every 'have
you reached'/ and 'be there in 20' texts/ I didn't sign up for this/ when at
twelve/ my mum brought me pretty scarves/ to grow into someday

JIM McELROY

# Hoor

*Hoor – Irish: used in both friendly and derogatory contexts.*

He called Widow Walsh *that poor oul hoor* –
in winter he'd send me up with fresh eggs;
next door, Joe McNab was *tight oul hoor,*
said he would count every bleedin' penny;
the *right oul hoors* lived on the Rock Hill,
I was let play with their *right wee hoors;*
passing pedlars, scammers – all *cute hoors,*
the tax man, a *connivin little hoor's bollix.*

I followed his hobnail crunch, oily overalls
round the farm – *annoyin his hoorin head*:
too many questions, go *ask your mother*;
at school, if I passed exams, he gave me
*right quick wee hoor*. Out on the moor,
neck veins bulging like baler twine,
he'd scrum hug boulders into position,
build ditches; at stubborn stones, sleeve
off brow sweat, stare at its granite belly,
christen it *a heavy oul hoor;* over lunch,
on top of stones, he'd share out soda farls,
cheddar slabs, pour our *cuppa tay,* tell me
to *thank your Mother;* as he lit his pipe,
he'd point out hedges needing trimmed,
the opening crops – ripening corn, barley.

When I left for the city, autumn's thresher
was gulping wheat sheafs; I watched him
grimace as he kneed obese seed bags up
to the trailer; through the belt slew, thrum,
he yelled *mind yourself* – to watch out for all

14

Jim McElroy

*them cute hoors*. Later that winter, the switch
put her call through, told me, *your mother's
on the line* – I was to *come home quick.*

Still in his overalls, he lay on the bed; fresh
muck clung to his hobnails; *right oul hoor*
found him slumped over granite; I bent down
for our first kiss – his *hoorin head,* cold as stone.

MARK FARLEY

# Three Candles

And I send him out to buy the balloon
And the cake.
And he says, it's just like last year.
And I tell him it's not.
And he says, we can't keep doing this.
And I give him a look.
And he shuts up.
And there's to be a 4 on the cake, I tell him.
And on the balloon.
And I call, remember the card!
And he slams his way to the van.
And I look to get the table ready,
And I find only three candles.
And I ring him up,
And he says, I'm doing it, I'm doing it.
And I say, we need another candle.
And he says he'll add it to the list.
And *she* doesn't want to come down,
And so I turn off the Wi-Fi,
And that makes her.
And we use the red tablecloth.
And then he comes back.
And the three of us light the candles.
And we tie the balloon to the chair.
And we sing the song.
And we say goodbye
                          again.

ALISON BINNEY

# The Way You Knew

the way you knew your own coat in the cloakroom    the way you knew as you
chewed how big the next bubble would be    the way everyone knew the new boy
was weird even before he began drinking ink    the way you knew how to share
crisps and when to and why it mattered    the way your bike always knew the way
home  the way you knew when to laugh and how much and who with   the way you
knew not to sit at the front    the way you knew when to put your hand up and why
no one did any more    the way you knew not to wear shoes like that    the way you
knew what *behind the bike sheds* meant before anyone said    the way everyone knew
who went    the way you knew the name carved on the desk wasn't yours but the *izza
lezza* made you go red    the way you knew not to wear your hair short        the way
you knew how to walk how to talk how to french kiss a boy and why you had to and
more      the way you knew for sure that if anyone knew about you you were dead

JOSHUA BLACKMAN

# Gameplay

I've tried everyone: the blacksmith, the butterfly boy,
the red-haired soprano on the farm, each
as oblique and uncertain
as the last, their riddles begetting riddles
so what now?

The elder speaks in a general sense
of honour, upheaval, of the past.
His bearded face (though pixelated)
is kingly. He is programmed to be kind.

I go back to the cave
     where I have spent
*so long*
shifting rocks
despatching all the bats
detonating bombs against various walls
to no end. (The explosions
kept me calm.)

Does anyone know where the amulet is?
Six likes, but of course
no help.

I watch the moon
as it grows
crueller by the day. I make deposits
at the bank.

*Music quickens.*

PENNY BOXALL

# Equity

I see her, evenings, in the new retirement flats
on the way to my mother's. The curtains
are always open, or there are no curtains,
and so there is no mystery. She's young for there.

She sits on the neat sofa, ankles crossed,
or writes neat letters at the bureau.
Sometimes there is a glass of champagne,
a single orchid. There are no visitors.

I have my suspicions. The space is anonymous
as a brochure: not a particle on the carpet;
cards wishing her a happy something
lined up faultless on the mantelpiece.

Easier to think she's on the payroll, Equity Card
tucked inside her model's-own purse.
Easier that than to accept she really lives
like this: all lights up, nothing to hide.

MARIE-LOUISE EYRES

# Tinder Box

Bugle weed and bee-blossoms catch
the sparks and pass the flames
lifted by the dry Santa Ana breeze
from black cottonwood to blue oak,
down to the shrubs of the chaparral.
The wind raises burning embers,
fireballs like giant orange poppies
until a mass of burning sagebrush on the hills
becomes the raging torch which no one can put out.

There are five roads leading out of Paradise
from highways to a one lane goat path,
neighbors wake each other with knocking,
stumbling through smoke and mayhem
honking cars and the calls of sirens,
they leave with nothing, no spoons
no combs, no dishes, no pills.

Dozens of fire trucks dot the landscape
helicopters dip through the sky
evacuees run down the streets
with sweating sour skins
escaping the ovens of their homes
to seek refuge in a cooling lake
and further south in Malibu, the icy sea.

Left behind is deadwood, dirt roads
charred timber structures, blackened hills
the warm and warped remains of mobile homes
with all the hope burned out –
smoldering empty acres, singed cats and dogs,
wandering deer, nickering horses
all fleeing toward the coast.

There a disheveled owl shuffles
cleaning her feathers in the sand,
a pet camel sits and blinks
by the steps of a lifeguard hut
waiting for fresh water, for rescue
this hazy morning on the beach
under the reddest of skies.

MARK FIDDES

# Assembling God (Flatpack Instructions)

Catalogue man kneels in a white room.
The slit in his drawn pecker-head smiles
but he's not happy at the sudden Arctic
filling up the frames in which he's stuck
in silence with crudely rendered tools.
Up next, a rough black cross says NO
to the screw-washer combination he grips.
He considers the best-selling Crucifix,
how it might have worked out differently
had Golgotha been planned by Ikea:
the Redeemer figure self-assembling,
slotting his cross-bar upside down,
thorns missing, the wrong size of nails,
starting from scratch, cheating with glue,
the Divine Intervention of Saint Velcro
for the flapping midriff modesty panel,
all the time refusing to ask for help.
Would the big religions be more forgiving
with just a wordless instruction manual
and a chirpy call center south of Cork?
The drawn man stacks his planks and slats,
but cannot find the pictogram reference
for blow torch or small incendiary device.
Next door, another man is hammering
like it's Asgard: soon there will be drills,
meat balls and whelps of marital bliss.
The drawn man feels like a surplus shelf
as the world's top-selling book case
slides gracefully, infinitely, sideways.

LANI O'HANLON

# Ghost Apples

In Michigan after a cold snap, freezing rain
coated the apples and hardened like toffee.

When the fruit thawed and slid through
the bottom, ice held those apple shapes,

transparent orbs hanging in the orchard.
Ghost apples the farmers called them.

In Ireland, an eleven-year-old girl takes
her own life and her mother sets up Hugg

so parents who lose their children
in this way can gather together,

their heads and arms and hearts
still holding the fruit.

SHARON PHILLIPS

# Epiphany

She's standing in the shower
thinking about sin and how
her children would cringe
if she wrote about lust

she sees how little shower gel
is left and wonders how need
shades to appetite then to greed
– she finds it hard to know
when one becomes the other –

and she carries on wondering
as she pulls on the dress
bought for next to nothing
then takes last night's bottles
to recycle and scrapes
leftovers into the bin

specifically if gluttony
derives from glut which relates
both to using and producing
too much and it seems – as
she hangs the washing out –
that both must be sinful
when so many are hungry

but it also occurs to her
that glut means glow
in German and she stops
to look at a red tulip
incandescent in the sun.

# Art History

Instead of painting red maple leaves,
Hokusai dipped the feet
Of a chicken in red paint.
He then chased the chicken
Across a large sheet of white paper,

To which he had added a line of blue
To represent the Tatsuta River.
The chicken behaved impeccably
Throughout, as did Hokusai,
Whose job it was to notice such things.

STEPHEN SPRATT

# Seeds

sown
as soon as
Persephone rolls
in from her big night out
into dark, alluvial soil will tend,
if the sky gods smile, to yield enough
to keep the indolent & simple minded alive,
& breed budding tyrants to battle for tiny crowns.
So tall spears rest in huts smelling of bread & beer while
famished farmers scratch their heads over the loss of the good
old days that can't now be reclaimed without a cull of the innocents,
sigh, domesticate beasts of burden & plough on through forests & deserts
& millennia of mud, felling, flooding, planting, exhausting, expanding across
oceans & continents & back again, extracting, adapting & proliferating as richer
crops increase the heartbeats a good harvest can support. These precarious lives need
luck every May from her Queen, offer Lugh first fruits & trap corn goddesses in dollies
to ensure they're around next year. But the old gods fade when ploughs accelerate through
enclosed & rotating fields that gobble up commons & little plots until carts, barges & trains
burst with grain & depleted soils are fertilised by islands of bird shit, nitrogen & ammonia &
crap tractors kill fantastic horses & Norin 10 doubles productivity again to 8 tons per hectare.
& we multiply too. Fast, but not so fast. 7.7 billion mouths to feed but food perhaps for 10, &
still 85,000 infants starve to death in Yemen & millions may soon exit through the same door.
Famine, when the old gods are dead, is not an Act of God. Sometimes it's just policy, as with
General von Trotha pinning the Herero in the desert to punish them, Stalin silencing the folk
music of Ukraine, or Saudi jets sending blue sambuks to the bottom of a red sea. At other
times it's dogma distilled into madness, like the Great Leap Forward, or a fusion of the
two when dogma is descended from Malthus & policy's devolved to zealous bean-
counters with views about lesser races. Bengal. Ireland. Nameless. Numberless.
Regardless of whether the black horse *could* have been thwarted it feels the
same: gnawing dread, draining strength, desperation, atrophy, apathy,
collapse, disease, darkness & flies. The good die first. Ties snap.
Speech lacks both meaning & breath, & perhaps it is this,
or the fear of it, that leads weary nomads to wonder
if life might be better with a bit more certainty.
Wonder if they should stop in some safe
spot where the grass grows tall.
Hang up the flint spears.
Dig a few holes.
Sow some
seeds.

KENNETH STEVEN

# Big Jim

Drives long distance lorries. Is gone
from Monday to Friday, sleeps anywhere
between Gateshead and Glasgow. Squeals back
into the yard to a flurry of children and shrieking.

Built like a brick with stickleback hair.
He *vrooms* old cars and thrums round corners.
He chops firewood as if the act
were cutting into chunks his wife's old boyfriends.

Brays at the kids. Sends them like scattered thistledown,
shrieking and shaking to crab through broken vans
or run to find the river. He jerks them in for dinner –
just sometimes marches home with bags of sweets.

Big Jim. Spends his weekends under bonnets
sharing cigarettes with jackals from the streets
who've got half jobs or jink off school
and dream of sliding out in Alfas with the chicks.

Yet early this Monday morning I saw him from the sink
under the big blustery blue of these June skies
in between the billows of the sheets all looped along the lines –
tenderly, secretly, kissing his wife goodbye.

ROSS FOSTER

# Henry

It came in a package a little bigger than a shoe box. As your daughter unwraps it, cutting cable ties and battling with vacuum sealed plastic, you notice a scene on the box lid not dissimilar to yours. A fresh-faced daughter and son presenting the small robot companion to a grateful grey-haired mother. You find yourself looking to that woman for a clue on how to act and reflexively force a smile.

The robot in question is cute enough. It reminds you of a children's toy you once bought your nephew, with its pixelated features on a screen carried around by tank-like tracks, which could surely navigate any terrain in your small suburban home. When your daughter, red-faced, finally retrieves the thing from its packaging it jumps to life. Its tracks flex on top of your daughter's hands. Its monitor, or face as you should probably call it, pivots slowly to you and back to your daughter. The pixels on its face line up to form a smile and words flash up in green text saying 'please show me around your home.'

'Fascinating little thing, isn't it?' Your daughter beams, noticing your smile but not its forced nature.

'Sarah got her father one last month and he's never been better. It'll let us know if you're in trouble. If you have a bit of a fall, that sort of thing. Saved Sarah's dad from a couple of close shaves I can tell you.'

You know she's trying to be supportive and caring, but what you hear is a chorus of your own weakness tinged with the slightest percussion of pity.

'Sounds like it will be a big help,' you say through your smile. 'Why does... why does it need a tour of the house?'

'Oh, Sarah told me about this. It needs to get the lay of the land so it knows what all the rooms are and where it's going. Clever, isn't it?'

You know she doesn't normally speak like this. This seeking approval. She was never that type of girl but she seeks it now.

'So clever,' you agree. Your daughter sets off with a smile giving the robot a guided tour as one would the queen. You hear her naming the rooms as she goes, filling in the gaps for the creature in her hands.

You poke at the bruise that started all this. Just a simple fall. Tripped over the vacuum you must have forgotten was there. It was the first time something like it had happened. 'A scare with Mom,' as your son had explained away to his boss on the phone as he dutifully kept you company when you got back from the hospital.

You thought nothing of it but were glad of the company. So much company. Your son and daughter would visit you twice, sometimes three times a week, which is unprecedented. You would make a show for them and have your leg resting on the coffee table just as they opened the door. They even brought the nephews and niece who would ooh and awe at the purplish blossom on your leg.

'All set up,' your daughter announces and places the automaton at your feet. The screen looks up at you and flashes a green pixelated smile.

'Thank you, dear,' you say. Really grateful this time but more for the thought than anything. 'What do I do with it?'

'Nothing, Mom. It looks after itself and will figure out what you need help with.' She reaches once more into the box and produces a small black bracelet. 'Here, put this on. It lets it keep track of your health and will give us a ring if anything is wrong.' The bracelet feels cold and uncomfortable but you let her put it on all the same.

'We really want to keep visiting you often but it's hard to make it up here every week with the kids. Now we'll know that you're safe.' Ahh, there it is, you think. The motive for the purchase. One robot equals fewer visits, and the memories of your usual level of relative solitude begin to creep back in.

'You'll still visit sometimes, won't you?' You say, attempting to be offhand and casual but fear you come across as desperate.

'Of course, Mom,' she assures, patting your hand. 'It's just a long way to come that's all and we can't keep an eye on you as much as we'd like.' There's a silence then. Filled with the push and pull of duty and affection.

'Now come on, you can't call it 'the robot' forever. What do you want to name it?'

'Henry,' you say, 'like the hoover.' It seems fitting, and as if giving a blessing your daughter smiles and presses a button on Henry's face to confirm.

You wave from the door as your daughter's Corolla turns out of the cul de sac. You think it's funny that she should say it's too far to come because she's the one that suggested you move here. To Cleobury Mortimer, which upon arrival you thought reeked of age and the very name of the place had a sense of the macabre – Mortimer, mortuary, mortal.

You sometimes long for your old house. No longer there now, but closer to your family and full of the years that came before. Pencil lines of varying heights on the kitchen door frame. The armchair in which your husband sat. The reading nook where you told him you were first expecting.

Henry is waiting for you when you return to the living room, right next to the seat you always sit in. It, or *he*, looks up at you dutifully like a hound and you can almost see a tail wagging and tongue hanging even though all he appears is a set of bright green eyes in the shape of upright chevrons, clearly meant to display some kind of happiness or domestication.

You ignore him, as you had planned to from the moment your daughter mentioned him. You are thankful that there is something to call for help if there is trouble but you don't plan on replacing necessary human contact for an LCD screen with arms. Instead of interacting with him you continue as normal. You sit down to read the latest romance novel from the local charity shop shelves. Taking a second to drink in the image of the muscular Spanish gentleman on the cover, you turn to a dog-eared page and all the lines are a blur. Once again, you've forgotten your glasses, most likely on the kitchen counter where you usually leave them while making tea for guests. As a younger person this would not inconvenience you, but with old bones and joints that pop like heated kernels you suddenly lose the will to read.

You hear a whistle at your feet, like bird song, and gaze down at Henry. Your reading glasses are balanced on his spindly hands and he's reaching up to you with a sort of visible effort. You take the glasses gently from their perch and say thank you. Now you feel foolish. Not only is Henry inanimate but you're also supposed to be taking a stand for your independence and here you are thanking him. His eyes blink into chevrons once again and he returns to his charging dock by the television; asleep but watchful. You need some escapism and give yourself completely to *Endless Desire*, surrendering to Spanish beaches and siestas.

You find yourself in your old home. You walk through the kitchen door and steady yourself on the door frame, fingers tracing the engraving of your son's height at age twelve scratched into the wood so hard as to leave an indent. George is sitting in his favourite armchair. His back to you but his voice strong.

'How's dinner coming along, love?'

There is a pot of something or other on the stove. It's bubbling over, water lashing at the flames of the gas burner.

'Everything alright?'

You want to go to him. It has been so long since you have seen his face but his voice is so clear, so present. The stove, though, is burning angrily.

With each rumble of the pot lid water spills over the sides and makes the flames dance and grow like the pot is full of bubbling lighter fluid. You start to smell smoke but move toward George instead of attending to the fire. Your hand is on his shoulder now but the fire is at your back and it's a heat you can still feel once you wake, *Endless Desire* splayed across your lap.

Henry is awake. Just watching. Ready to react to a level of beats per minute that would justify calling your daughter or the ambulance. You slow your breathing and he relaxes. His face recedes to its regular position but he drives over to your feet and sits there. You reach for the tape recorder on the side table, as you do whenever you have this dream. You rewind to the beginning and play the tape.

'Hello, love. So sorry I missed you again but I won't be out here for much longer. They've got us working some long hours at the steelworks but they've got some new starters coming in soon so I can move back home again and work just down the road as always. I miss you but we both know I can't keep working forever and the extra pay from this job should set us up nicely. Maybe we can even go on that cruise we talked about? The one through the Fjords? Either way, we should get away together when I get back. Just you and me. I don't care if we go to Switzerland or super-Mare.

'I hope you're getting on without me, just not too well. See you soon. I love you.'

You have listened to the tape many times. You know the breaths, pauses and the rhythm of the words like you know the melody of your favourite songs. It calms you in moments like these and is the only link to him that wasn't taken by the flames.

\*\*\*

Two weeks pass and though you hate to say it, Henry has grown on you. He helps you cook and clean where he can, wakes you when you need waking and as such is very useful but occasionally very annoying. Though you're warming to him, it has been two weeks without a call from your family and you still can't bring yourself to talk to a robot. So you've decided to walk the next door neighbour's dogs. The neighbours are less mobile than you and the whole cul de sac pays the price through the dog's incessant barking. You need to keep your leg moving, you tell them, and they're only too happy to oblige. Harry and Sally do not like each other as much as their Hollywood counterparts and you have to separate them by holding one leash in each hand and making sure they follow their own tracks. They are both Pomeranians, which delights you. You see them as beige clouds of fluff on leashes and they get you out of the house. Everyone in the cul de sac is getting a better night's sleep because of it.

You drop off Harry and Sally and return home, where Henry is waiting for you at the door. He flashes his eyes, gives a green smile and pushes your slippers up to your feet.

'Thank you,' you say, no longer feeling foolish.

One thing the dogs bring with them is the memory of conversations. You and George had always wanted a dog but could never find the right time. You wonder about getting one now but don't think it would be right without him. It's in these moments you listen to the tape again, as you have nearly every day for the past two weeks. 'I have been spoiled by injury,' you think. You are sure you weren't so needy before the accident but now you long for your family as you did in those first few months after your husband's death. In place of your son, your daughter and your nephews you now have this tape of your husband and a small robot you named after a vacuum cleaner. You remove the tape from the recorder and place it on the coffee table, hoping that this small inconvenience will deter you from relying on it again. Calling your family only ever seems to bother them. They have work or they're running after the kids or are at last sitting down with nothing to do only to be interrupted by your call. You can see your daughter pick up her phone and see your name on the caller ID. She groans, rubs her eyes and answers with fake enthusiasm. That is not what you want.

There is, however, another method. You think back to Henry's reaction after each of your dreams. The look of poise and a readiness to call for help. You move to the kitchen, no longer constrained by the limp that has slowed you for over a month. You want to make a small impact. Nothing to worry about but just enough to create a fuss. You see a knife in the block that you no longer use. It's incredibly sharp and almost new. It would only take a prick, you think. You can already feel your blood pulsing, which means Henry must be aware. You listen for the quiet rumble of his tracks rolling across the floor. You must act before he is in the room or not at all. You flinch from the knife's cold steel handle yet still raise it to your finger. It has to look like something natural. A kitchen injury. Vegetables chopped too furiously. An honest mistake by an old woman becoming less coordinated with age. Henry is just behind the door now. You can hear him repositioning in an attempt to push through the open crack. You place the blade on the tip of your index finger and feel the friction. Just one push. A little pressure. Easy. Quick. A release of blood.

But you can't. And at that moment Henry bursts through the door and looks from you to the knife and back to the knife again. He thinks for a moment, if that is a thing he does, and moves towards the fridge to get ingredients for lunch. You laugh, but tears fall down your cheeks all the same.

More time passes and it seems your family have forgotten you altogether. Harry and Sally, they pine for you, wait for you, are sad when you leave. You go and pick them up for their daily walk and the neighbours tell you they're going to the shops.

'You can take them now if you like but you might have to keep them at your place if we're not back. Sorry about that.'

'Don't worry,' you say, 'probably overdue anyway.'

You are getting stronger now and the walks are getting longer. By the end of it the Pomeranians are more tired than you. They collapse on the driveway like coughed-up hairballs. The neighbours are not back yet, so you pick up the exhausted canines and take them to your living room. You have chicken in the fridge and go to fetch them a little food and water. Henry follows you, scared of being made a plaything by the two dogs. As you're filling the bowls you hear a slight rustle and commotion from the living room but think nothing of it. The dogs are far too tired to be mischievous.

Returning to the living room you see the result of the commotion. Harry and Sally playing tug of war with the tape, its innards a hopeless tangle. You put the bowls down where you stand and water soaks the carpet. The dogs flee as you lunge towards them, knowing they've done wrong. You assess the damage. The case is a little cracked and the tape is unspooled, broken in places. You wind the tape all the same and attempt to play it through the recorder, but it is still cracked and sodden with dog spit.

You cry then. Shaking. It is a similar cry as when you lost a loved one. You feel as if you are emptying. The dogs feast on the chicken and lick the water from the beige carpet. Henry calls your daughter. You can hear it ringing.

'Mom? Mom are you alright? Mom?' You quiet your crying to a murmur and wait until your daughter gives up.

'Sorry we haven't been around for a while but it has been so busy at work. Mom? Well, I'll call you later to make sure you're okay.'

Your daughter's voice stops coming out of Henry. You wipe your eyes and take the dogs back next door without a word.

'Are you alright?' The husband says, but you don't answer.

You do your best to fix the tape when you get back and finally a crackle erupts from the recorder but the tape catches and skips, and through it all you can't hear him.

Henry does not attempt to call your daughter again. You rewind and play, rewind and play, rewind and play again and again but nothing changes. You finally stop.

'Hello love,' you hear, not knowing if it's a memory or George himself descended from somewhere you don't believe in.

'I'm so sorry I missed you again.' Henry says in a familiar voice, his eyes flashing green chevrons.

SULAXANA HIPPISLEY

# The Quarter Loaf

The boy and the girl arrived at Chooty's house flat bang in the middle of a bread and sugar afternoon. But it wasn't her house. Not exactly, for the house on the hill belonged to Chooty's uncle and his wife Sandhya. She and Ammi had come to live there some six weeks earlier when the troubles began. 'Watch your mouth, watch your step and for goodness sake, don't call it *your* house before your aunt!' Ammi hissed at her every morning. In Chooty's eyes, that was the beginning. And you couldn't choose beginnings. They chose you. Like uninvited guests that barged through the door at a party and demanded an explanation; they chose you, whether you liked it or not.

The trouble, as all the adults called it, was a funny thing. All Chooty knew was that the schools were shut and the buses had stopped and there was bread and sugar for lunch and dinner every day. This, indisputably, was the best thing about the trouble, Chooty thought. She liked thick slices of bakery bread with a coating of Astra margarine and a fine dusting of sugar, just enough for a crunch between the teeth. She preferred it by far to the Prima bread in its red and white cellophane bag that they used to buy at Food City on the way home from school. She didn't miss those thin slices that vanished in your mouth or congealed shut and turned soggy with the tiniest layer of jam in your lunch box on a hot day. But Ammi grumbled every night about being given a room above the kitchen and never partook in these delights. She pushed her plate at Chooty, swallowed scorching black tea and licked her sugar straight from the palm.

It was one o'clock in the afternoon and Chooty shifted from foot to foot behind the slit in the doorway. She pressed a hand against the panel on her dress to quieten the howl of her belly. All you had to do was breathe in tight to stop this noise or any other noise your body tried to make when you were in Sandhya Aunty's parlour. This was one rule she knew for certain. On any other day, Ammi would have called her by now. Without that sugary panacea on a Donald Duck plate, Chooty wondered how Ammi would silence the thousand questions she liked to ask. What happened to the driver of the 112 bus? Why do we turn out the lights at seven o'clock? Why can't we go into Kandy? What did I do to make you so angry all the time? Obviously, Ammi had forgotten. But there they all were, standing in the parlour, quite still with furrowed brows, staring at the boy and the girl. Adults were odd nowadays, the way they would swing between reproaching every move you made one minute and forgetting that you existed altogether the next. Chooty wondered whether she should say something or remind them about lunch. She considered pointing to the GMT window on her red Mickey Mouse digital watch and telling them about her father in London who was probably eating chocolate and red apples for breakfast as they spoke. Then she remembered that it was exactly this sort of smart pandit style remark that Ammi had warned her to keep firmly to herself. 'Nobody,' she said, 'nobody likes little girls who ripen before their time.'

She decided the girl was pretty. But not in a way that anyone else would have recognised. Not in 1988 anyhow. Years later, when Chooty would try to piece together the shape of her face, each feature would refuse to comply with her compositions. She had a long nose and a gap between the teeth that was only visible when she smiled properly. As her lips parted, you saw childhood lingering in the corners of her mouth; she was, without a doubt, one of those people who could crunch hard Delta toffee on the sly. Chooty watched as the girl ran her sari pota through her fingers, never lifting her eyes to meet the gaze of those around her. The tiny straps on her white sandals were dashed with specks of mud and a sports bag, swollen to bursting, sat by her feet. Chooty thought she looked like one of the girls from upper school who walked arm in arm with others or giggled at the bus stop while they chewed peanuts from paper cornets and spat the shells on the ground. They wore knee length socks those girls. In high school, she would wear knee length socks and eat plenty of peanuts at the bus stop because Ammi wouldn't be there. And maybe tamarind pods too or Kiss Kiss or salted pineapple with chilli, the ones Ammi told her were dirty because you never knew where those market people came from and if they washed their hands.

Next to the girl sat a boy, maybe a few years older. Now him, Chooty knew him. He was Bandula, Sandhya Aunty's younger brother. She remembered him visiting once before her father went to England. With his curly hair and gold chains, Chooty thought he looked like one of those cricket players or the man from the toothpaste advert. He had a wide shiny smile, called her 'Chutta' and placed a large box of chocolate bites in her hands. Maybe somewhere in that bag, she thought. Just maybe....but today he wasn't smiling. Not even a little bit. Just then, Sandhya Aunty broke the silence. 'Does anybody know? Amma?'

Uncle Bandula shook his head quickly. 'No-one. We had nowhere else to go.'

'Chooty!' hissed a voice from behind. She felt a familiar grip on her arm. 'Come here!'

\*\*\*

'How could he Akka? How could he?' Sandhya Aunty and Ammi were trying to whisper in the kitchen. Between their words came the stop and start roar of the coconut grater. Chooty sat on the bottom step wondering when her bread would arrive. It was 1.45 now and she wasn't meant to hear a word. Not one. But it turned out that Sandhya Aunty was very bad at whispering. Very bad.

'Eloped! With a servant's daughter! How can he look my parents in the eye, marrying her? All that education! Trinity, Captain of the cricket team and Dubai! Wasted. All gone. Those people, her parents, *still* live in that house with the *dung* walls by the river.'

'I know nangi,' Ammi said. 'But it's done now. He's married her. What can you do?'

Chooty heard the sharp intake of Sandhya Aunty's breath. She could almost see the nostrils flaring before whatever punishment she had in mind was meted out.

'I have half a mind to –'.

'Turn them away? At a time like this? Where will they go? No buses to Kandy for six miles and they've walked at least seven to get here. Think nangi, think,' Ammi said.

'What do they think we are? They must think we're living like kings. Look at the store cupboard. Rice enough for a week. Maybe two. Shops shut and no more gas cylinders.'

'It's done now. Give them lunch. Let them stay tonight and then they'll see how bad things are here.'

'I'll have to think of something,' Sandhya said. 'And Chathu he calls her. What kind of name is Chathuri for a low caste girl?'

Chooty thought that Chathuri was a perfect name. It made her think of the nice smelling things that she had seen on Sandhya Aunty's dresser, things she was forbidden to touch: bottles with rose shaped lids and peach clams with mirrors that enlarged your nose a thousand times. And married. Bandula and Chathu were married. The word left a fizz of

37

electricity at her fingertips and all of a sudden, for a reason she couldn't explain, Chooty felt shy.

Slip-slap of sandals from the side of the house. Chooty looked up. There they were, the new bride and groom venturing down the steps towards the well at the bottom of the garden. Chooty followed them through the grilled windows overlooking the courtyard. Chathu moved behind her husband's heels like a stray pup eager not to part from a new owner. They had threadbare towels flung over their shoulders, the thin ones with garish yellow and blue checks that you could buy at the market for a rupee. In their hands, bright green soap boxes blazed in the afternoon sun. At the well, Chathu's eyes drifted over the high branches of the coconut trees whilst Bandula reached down to retrieve the tin pail. Chooty heard it clang against the rocks as he lowered it into the well. Months later, when the torpor of those hot afternoons failed to stir a single living thing, she would hear the clang again. But by then, no one else could hear it apart from her.

She watched them now, standing beneath the light that pierced the coconut branches. They did all the things that you were supposed to do, like brush your teeth and wash under your arms and the soles of your feet. But at the same time, it was different from when Ammi did it with her. There was no scrubbing or berating. Even as Bandula poured water from the pail into Chathu's cupped hands, it didn't seem like water at all, but another liquid possessed of a power not known to mere mortals. These otherwise perfunctory gestures, ablutions, the first marital rites, were things, Chooty realised, that you weren't supposed to see, because they belonged to that other world. The 'married' world hinted at in soap adverts when a girl was seen pressing her nose into the bud of a flower or when Ammi pinched her arm for staring at a couple on a bench in Vihara Maha Devi park. And they weren't doing anything except drinking Coca-cola from the same bottle. Now it was all here, unfolding before her like an evening tele-drama and no one would stop her from watching. Not even Ammi. In such times, Chooty decided, when everyone had long forgotten long division, the exercises from 'The Radiant Way,' and the rest of her schoolbooks, there were things you could still learn.

\*\*\*

An hour after lunch, Chooty paced twice, three times before Bandula and Chathu's room at the top of the stairs, listening out for the hums and whispers that seeped through the curtain. Sandhya Aunty had given them Chooty's late grandfather's room, a dark cave still lined with the residue

38

of death. She had only gone in there once with Ammi during a power cut to find the flash light he kept by his bed and remembered the piles of yellowing newspapers, the tins of boot polish peeking from under the wardrobe and the shelves packed with Whitaker's Almanacs. And that cloying smell like sweat mixed with incense. She had been in no hurry then to return to that room but now she could think of nowhere else she would rather be. Through the parting in the curtain, she caught a glimpse of Bandula's soles resting on the mattress, cracked and whitish around the heel. Chathu was bent over a suitcase on the bed, saying something inaudible and raising a bright printed dress to her eyes for close inspection. And then she saw her. Chooty gasped and padded backwards but it was too late. Chathu was walking towards the doorway.

'Ay? How are you? Want to come in?' Chathu smiled at her. 'Come on. Are you shy?' Chooty shook her head. In her pink nylon dress with bluebirds, she seemed a little older than the woman that had sat in the parlour. Chathu stretched out her hand. 'Please?'

'Ammi will tell me off,' Chooty said, biting her lip. It was true. Nothing other than a mouthful from Ammi lay in wait if she was going to dabble in grown up love business like this.

'I won't tell,' Chathu said.

She followed Chathu through the parting in the curtain. Bandula raised himself on the bed as she entered. 'Hullo Chutta!' he said. 'Kohomada? You're getting big now. Not a Chutta anymore! This one was only six when I last saw her.'

'Seven,' Chooty corrected him.

'Oh-ho, so now you can speak?' Bandula said with a laugh. 'I saw you out there. Waiting to play with us, no? Or spying?'

Chooty pressed her face against the curve of Chathu's waist. A feint trace of Rexona soap and hair oil. 'It's ok, we're not going to tell,' Chathu said. 'Stay with us, talk to us.' She patted Chooty's cheek softly and cleared a space on the bed beside the open suitcase. She liked sitting in the lull between them, looking out for signs of something that she couldn't quite name: a laugh, a touch, a knowing look. But the newlyweds didn't seem to care for such things. Chathu closed the lid of her case, sat on the bed and then stood almost as soon the mattress creaked beneath her. They seemed nervous, restless. On a lone patch of a dresser, Chathu had marked her territory: talcum powder, a small bottle of Debutante and two combs in a plastic case. But these things seemed to shrink under the glare of the newspapers and the boot polish that still peered at the interlopers from beneath the dresser. Chooty looked away.

'So,' Bandula said, 'is it nice being in the big house?'

Chooty shook her head and then remembered that it was best to say nothing when adults asked for your opinions. She nodded. Fast.

'Mhmm, I don't believe you. Is it big aunty Sandhya? She's a big fat loud mouth no? Hippopotamus no?' And suddenly she was nodding in agreement. Yes, she is, Chooty longed to say. I hate her. I hate everyone. Even Ammi. Suddenly the springs creaked beneath him too as Bandula chuckled into his pillow. 'Bandula!' Chathu hissed in mock reproach. 'She'll hear us!'

'Come Chooty, come,' he was beckoning her now. Pillow creases ran across his cheek and white hairs peeked at his temples. He wasn't so shiny or handsome as she remembered. 'I'll tell you a secret,' he whispered. 'I don't like my big sister either.' With that, he smiled his toothpaste advert grin and patted her head. 'Tell you what, while we're here, you come and play with us. We'll hide you under the bed if she comes looking for you.' The prospect of being protected from the daily nagging and indignities she suffered seemed too good to be true. But before Chooty could reply, a familiar voice bellowed from the hallway.

'Bandula? Come out here a minute will you?' It was Sandhya Aunty. Bile rose in her throat as she gripped the bedpost. Chathu too seemed to be stupefied by the sound, her eyes unblinking, fixed on the doorway as though Sandhya might burst in. Bandula bounded out of bed towards the door.

'Akka?'

'I'm going to the bakery. It's only open for an hour and will close at four. There'll be a queue and Manolis saves a good loaf for me at the back so...'

'Oh. Well, we'll go. Don't trouble yourself. Let us go,' Chooty heard Bandula say.

'Yes, we'll go. It's the least we can do,' Chathu joined them now and Chooty stood at the foot of the bed, watching Sandhya Aunty's face through the curtain. For a moment, Sandhya Aunty looked at Bandula and Chathu as though they had offered to remove one of her limbs.

\*\*\*

Chooty walked on the centre of the warm tarmac while Chathu and Bandula followed behind. She stretched out her arms. The road was hers all alone. Once in a while, she moved to the side as a local boy shuttled past with the single bell of his bike. Apart from that, she couldn't remember when she had last seen a bus or a lorry pass on the main road. Uncle Herath said that it wasn't because of the strikes anymore but the transport blockade that the government had put in place to stop the trouble. Either way, something hung in the air. Chooty wanted to touch it. She could taste it on her tongue, like the static crackle a minute before the fireworks were set off at New Year. It felt like a Sunday or a Friday or maybe a holiday. The truth was that without school and television and the bus rides into town, she couldn't tell what day of the week it was. One day merged into the next, punctuated only by the hush hush news that no one bothered to tell her. Doors remained shut all along the road and Chooty knew that most children, like her, were barricaded indoors in the heat. She waved at Mr Peiris who still liked to brave the outdoors and sit on the veranda to read his paper or prune his Bougainvillea. But Sandhya Aunty said that was because he was a Christian and no one had a grudge against him.

On the corner, Chooty stopped to point at the gutted remains of the municipal office. 'Look Bandula maama! Look!' she cried. Five days after the firebombing, the smoke was still rising from the teak beams that once ran across the roof. They leaned through a window of one of the remaining walls. 'Appo, look at this!' Chathu clamped a hand over her mouth. Chooty felt her other hand coming to rest on her own head. 'And you saw this?' she asked.

Chooty nodded. 'It burned all night and all the next day and even the day after they brought the water.'

The inside though was just ash and shapes of things that you could once use and couldn't anymore. Chooty spotted a fan whose blades had congealed into black lumps under the heat. Then there were the metal chairs whose seats had burnt away, waiting like sitting skeletons for a bus that would never come. On the last day, when the fire had died down, all the other local children crept in and salvaged things – boxes of pens, old ledgers and even paper clips. She had seen them walking down the road, laughing, carrying their booty in armloads as Ammi tutted about their thieving parents. She saw something glimmering now. A silver bell sat immaculate on the ground amidst the rubble like a ministering angel. She longed to press that bell and hear it trill. Just once.

At the top of the road, Chooty saw that a queue had started to form. It snaked along the pavement all the way past the post office. They joined it hurriedly. Chooty had never stood in the bread line before. All at once, she felt important that the duty of bringing home the evening loaf had fallen, if partly, upon her. The women in the queue had straw bags tucked under their arms and Chooty waved 'hello' to Soma and Laisa, the servant girls who had stopped coming weeks earlier. They smiled at Bandula but said nothing to Chathu who stood beside him biting the nails on her left hand.

Soon, Manolis opened the window and the queue began to move. Chooty gripped Chathu's hand and peered around the side. She liked the way that Chathu slipped fingers in between hers as though they were friends, as though they had secrets to tell and funny stories to share and the way that their clasped hands would swing backwards and forwards in time to a song no one else could hear. Finally, it was their turn. Manolis stood before a counter of loaves, poised with a large knife in hand. Next to him, Chooty saw a small boy with a stack of newspaper pages ready to wrap each loaf. The boy worked quickly and she watched as his deft fingers turned the loaves into meticulous rectangles of possibility. You could play a guessing game then and think it wasn't bread but a Swiss roll or box of Maliban cookies. Chooty sighed and noticed that the jars before them were empty too. Usually they were full of sticky Kimbula bread glazed with sugar that would stick to the roof of your mouth. 'Next!' cried Manolis.

Before Bandula or Chooty could utter a word, Chathu piped up. 'Give me a quarter loaf!' she said. Manolis looked at her for a moment and then sliced a neat quarter of the loaf before him. Chooty felt Bandula stiffen next to her as he reached into his pocket.

\*\*\*

By the time they turned the corner, Chooty saw Ammi standing by the gate, her arms folded behind her. She knew then that it was all wrong, all of it, everything she had done that afternoon. Ammi marched towards them with wide strides and grabbed Chooty's arm.

'Ow Ammi, you're hurting me, ow!' she cried.

'Did I say you could go with them? Did I?' she said through gritted teeth. Chooty blinked hard. She felt a familiar heat rising across her face as Ammi pulled her away towards the stone steps that led down to the room below. She knelt by the tap beside the kitchen and thrust Chooty's hand under the running water. 'Wash your hands! How could you hold hands with her! And going off like that without telling me!' Chooty watched in silence as tears blurred the tap, the water and her mother's face into one quivering mass.

\*\*\*

By seven o'clock that evening, her cheeks were sore from weeping. It hadn't helped that Ammi had washed her face with a bar of soap that seemed to strip away an entire layer of her skin. She sat at the dining table, scrubbed clean of sin with a blue Donald Duck plate before her. For the first time, she noticed that Donald's left eye was fading as fast as the ribbon in his cap. Only a year earlier, she, Ammi and her father had gone to Colombo and she had chosen the plate from a shop with glass cabinets. Then the plate rode home on her lap, wrapped in a paper bag that carried with it the delicious scent of new dolls, crisp notebooks and the start of school. Suddenly, it all seemed so far away, school and her father and a time where going into a shop or wanting something did not seem like an act that others had the right over.

Her stomach rumbled noisily but she was going to try her best to resist eating. A hunger strike: that would show Ammi for the scolding. A scolding which in her eyes seemed disproportionate to the crime in question. She wondered how long she would last before they resorted to force-feeding. Maybe a week? A day? At Katharagma she had seen those pu-sari men with matted hair and bony ribs. Some of them didn't eat for months, years even. She would find a tree, sit beneath it and others would come to watch her starve. How hard could it be? That would show Ammi, it really would.

'Where's your mother?' said a voice.

Sandhya Aunty stood before her with the package from the bakers in her left hand. She thrust it onto the table and shook her head. Chooty shrugged. Best not to speak at times like this, she thought. Sandhya sighed heavily. 'Wait till your mother sees this,' she said as she disappeared into the hallway. From the corner of her eyes, Chooty saw the flicker of a shape at the top of the stairs. It was Chathu, who now peered down at her with a look of concern. Chooty managed a little wave and a smile. If Bandula had kept his promise, she would find them both later and tell them everything. Everything would be all right in that room and Chathu might let her sit on the bed again and touch a thing or two from the dresser.

Now Ammi came into the dining room with Sandhya Aunty at her heels. 'Wait, let me see,' Ammi was saying as she hurried towards the bread package on the table. Sandhya Aunty hovered over her shoulder as Ammi unwrapped the parcel with anthropological interest. They both stood back. The quarter loaf now sat at the centre of the newspaper, staring at Chooty. Its gaping white inside had shrivelled under the heat.

'So it's true, she bought a quarter loaf!' Ammi whispered as a hand flew to her mouth.

'Yes Akka,' Sandhya Aunty said with a little laugh. 'You see, imagine someone from our house going to Manolis to ask for a quarter loaf? Imagine! Chee! And now this is the woman our Bandula is with. Can you

43

imagine a house that buys quarter loaves?' Their shoulders were rising now as laughter invaded their bodies. It was such a strange thing to see her mother laughing in great unfathomable hiccups that Chooty did not know what to say. When had she last laughed like that? She couldn't remember a single day before or after when it happened again.

But Chooty did not laugh. Out of the corner of her eye, she saw a shape disappear up the stairs: a flash of pink vanishing from the railings like the sudden flight of a bird.

\*\*\*

In the years that followed, Chooty would play the day again in her mind and find herself suspended between those hours and the dawn that followed. It was there that she liked to reside. Sometimes, she would wake from her dreams and imagine that they were still upstairs, Chathu and Bandula, sitting amidst the decay of that deathly room and the newness of their vows. Other times, she would wake thinking that they had gone down to the well again with soapboxes blazing in their hands like grenades. Then, as she grew older, much older than Chathu had been then that day, she altered the ending to suit the hue of her thoughts: they had gone out to buy another loaf or they had received a mysterious telegram in the middle of the night about a bus that could ferry them away with a hoard of other newly married elopers. But in truth, she knew that there were no buses, no telephones or messages or any semblance of a thing that had the potential to alter the course of their lives.

Then, on some days, Chooty woke with the knowledge that she and everyone else had the following morning. That they had left at dawn without a reason, without a goodbye and ventured out into a world from which no one would ever hear of them again. Sometimes, she wondered whether it was her going with them to the bakers, giddy with excitement that had made Chathu call out for that loaf. If only she had refused to go with them or told her that no one ever ate quarter loaves in their house, Chathu would have given her a doe-eyed smile and thanked her.

After a few hours, when it was clear that they were not going to return, the local police superintendent turned up at Sandhya Aunty's request. Ammi kept Chooty downstairs with a thick slice of bread, evenly coated with butter (not margarine) and sprinkled with just the right amount of sugar. Chooty imagined his khaki bottom on the chair that Chathu had sat on the day before, his sweaty posterior squashing the imprint of her figure. By then, the bread had turned into stony lumps in her throat. After that day, she did not ask for bread and sugar again.

Once the toing and froing from the Police station stopped, neither Ammi nor Sandhya Aunty could utter their names. In those days, the police had bigger matters to deal with than the elopements of upper middle class folk. Every other house was missing a girl or a boy who had gone to work or school and had been caught in a rally or a mass arrest from which they never returned home. Sometimes, when she looked back at the gauntness of those days, Chooty saw something else beyond the fire bombings and unmarked graves: hunger forming the hard lines on her mother's face.

Long after that year was over and everyone had forgotten the charred remains of the country that she and others left behind, Chooty would catch glimpses of them. Sometimes, a couple at a bus stop exchanging the glances of first courtship would conjure them into being. Or she would seek them out at a cinema in Hounslow, a lanky Amir Khan convincing Juhi Chawla to elope with him only to meet their fate at the end of a knife. Then she would build the tapestry alone in bed whenever the dawn failed to come or whilst recoiling from the arms of a lover. The boy's hands cup water from a spluttering roadside tap for the girl to drink. Afterwards, they cross a stream. Her skinny fingers hook into the belt of his jeans. Then, they lean heads at an abandoned bus shelter, dank with urine and a peeling poster of the president behind them. After that, there's nothing but the sound of their breath and a lilac sky with parting stars, blinking at them like fireflies in the dust.

ANNA METCALFE

# Start Again

I am looking out of the window when my boss comes in. He sits on the end of my desk and blocks out the light. He is feeling kind towards me today. He wants to check if I'm all right because it's been a difficult week. The day before yesterday, there was a violent incident. A fight broke out. It's been playing on my mind but I tell him I'm fine. His hair is dark and thin and he's wearing a blue suit. The fit is wrong but I'm not sure if it's too big or too small, whether he looks too big or too small inside it. He turns to face me.

'You've got a kid, right?' he says.

I tell him that her name is Jemima and that she's three and a half.

I don't know why, but he finds this funny. He chuckles to himself without looking at me. Maybe he's thinking of his own children, the silly things they did at that age. I couldn't tell you for sure whether or not he has children because it's not the kind of thing I would ask.

After a pause, he says that if I'm really okay then he'll let me get on with my work. When he stands up, the light slips back over the desk like water.

There's a hunger strike on at the moment. That's partly why tensions are so high, and why my boss is wandering the hallways checking on us. It's natural, I think, that during a protest the women would become more hopeful. And it sounds like a good thing, to have hope, but right now I'm not so sure. If it doesn't work, if their demands are not met, then the come-down will be hard. All that effort will be for nothing, starving themselves only to find that no one cares.

\*\*\*

On Saturday mornings, if I'm not working, Jemima and I play a game called *Where Are You?* We play it in bed, sitting up with the covers domed over us. It starts with her thinking of a place, then she takes a moment to imagine herself there. Sometimes she gives it away by asking me questions – *Mummy, are there cats in space? Can you get hot chocolate*

46

*on the beach?* Otherwise, I have to guess where she is. She doesn't give me any clues. I just guess and guess, and she says *no, no, no,* with a mysterious smile on her face. Afterwards, when I've got it right, she'll tell me what it was like.

She doesn't know a lot of different countries yet, so she chooses the places she's seen in books or on TV. *Mummy, I was looking around Venus and it was cold and I had to shout so loudly to make myself heard over all the space noise. Mummy, I was up in the air on a cloud and there was a whole city of clouds, and I was part-cloud, part-girl, because that's what it's like when you live on a cloud. Mummy I was at the bottom of the sea and I helped an octopus dig a hole but the octopus said I was useless because I just didn't have enough arms.* There's always some unexpected detail. She never tells it how I think she will. Sometimes I worry how much she enjoys it, telling me that she's been very far away.

***

I have a stack of yellow forms to fill out. Whenever someone skips a meal we have to write it down. There's a box for their name and their detainee number, then a box to say which meal was missed. At the end there's a space to add up the total number of days they've been without food. A few of the women are also refusing water. I make a note of that in red pen. After a while, we have to fill out more forms because then there's *considerable medical risk.* All in all, now that most of them are refusing food several times a day, there is a lot more paperwork to do.

If I think too long about the strike, I start to feel a kind of emptiness in my own body. Sometimes it's just a hollowness in the stomach, at other times it becomes a weakening in the arms and legs. I'm interested in how it happens, how thinking about something can make it real. As well as filling out the yellow forms, we're obliged to provide the women who are on strike with medical information about the consequences of food deprivation. There are numerous side effects – low electrolyte levels, dizziness, feeling cold all the time, decelerated heart rate, muscle weakness, fatigue, malnutrition, chronic diarrhoea. We slide leaflets under their bedroom doors or, if they're willing to talk, we explain it to them face to face. Sometimes, I'll be sitting on someone's bed, listing the various consequences of prolonged starvation and whoever's bed it is will tell me that they haven't eaten in three days. I'll say that they might be experiencing some feelings of dizziness and disorientation and as I say it my eyesight will start to blur. I'll have to hold onto the frame to steady myself. It's quite out of character for me. I'm not a very sympathetic person.

A few months ago, someone came to interview us. It was part of a big inquiry. One of the interviewer's questions struck me as particularly odd.

'When was it that you became so disaffected?' the interviewer asked. We were sitting in the boss's office. I guess he had given it to her to use. I couldn't help but feel I was being reprimanded for something, that some kind of punishment was about to be doled out. I remember wrapping my arms around myself without consciously deciding to do it, and then I told her that I didn't think *disaffected* was the right word. She asked me what word I would prefer. I must have thought about it for a long time because she started tapping her pencil against her notebook and jiggling her leg. My whole body tensed. I told her the right word was *distanced*. I was *at a distance* from it all.

While I'm filling out the yellow forms, I try to keep myself at a distance from the words. It's a relief to get to the end. I find that even when things are unpleasant there can be satisfaction in a task well done.

Marta comes in while I'm putting the paperwork away.

'It's starting,' she says.

'What is?' I ask.

'The demonstration,' she says. 'Did you forget?'

'It's okay,' I tell her. 'I parked around the back.'

Marta says that I'm smart. 'Fucking moralists,' she says.

I don't like it when she swears, though I'm not against swearing in general. Perhaps it's the word 'moralists' I'm objecting to. I don't want to be excluded from that group.

She sits down and pulls the ring off a Diet Coke. 'What time do you finish today?'

I tell her five thirty.

Marta rolls her eyes. 'The dream,' she says bitterly. 'A normal fucking shift.'

She's right. It is the dream. I've promised Jemima spaghetti. She likes it with lentils and boiled carrots because she already knows what's good for her.

***

Most of the time, I try not to think about Jemima at work. I don't have a picture of her on my desk. Likewise, I try not to think about work when I'm with Jemima at home. I give her my whole attention and leave no room for anything else. I touch her hot sticky cheeks and wipe her wet dripping nose. I listen to her short breaths and wait for her hands to find my face. Whenever she moves, speaks, laughs, cries, anytime she does anything, I feel differently in my own skin.

Like a lot of kids, Jemima sometimes gets scared of things she can't see. I used to be the same. When I was young, I was frightened of the monsters in the basement, the shadowy ghosts in the mirrors. But Jemima isn't scared of monsters or ghosts and she isn't frightened for herself. She says she can hear things in the furniture, small creatures that can't get out. When I ask her what they are she always says she doesn't know. 'Just small enough to fit,' she suggests. 'Small enough to get inside.'

A few weeks ago we were sitting at the kitchen table when out of nowhere she started to cry. She put a hand on the vinyl cloth then leaned in until her ear was close to the table's surface.

'They're in there,' she mumbled between sobs. 'I can hear the small things.'

'But the table is big,' I said to her.

'It's not,' she said. 'I could never fit in there.'

'Big-small then,' I said, smiling.

'Big-small,' she said, still sobbing, and then she held her arms out towards me. 'Yes. Big-small.'

*Big-small* is a joke of ours, a thing we do. I took her on my lap and waited for her to cry herself out. When she became calmer, she put her hands on the table again and looked at me.

'I believe you,' I told her, and maybe I did.

She peeled her palms off the cloth, making a slow and sticky sound, and then she covered her eyes. 'They told me,' she said. 'They're gasping for the air.'

I asked her what she wanted me to do.

She thought for a moment, then she said quite cheerfully: 'We'll break it open and start again.'

***

It's Marta's job to write a report about the violent incident of the day before yesterday. It should have been done much earlier, but nobody wanted to take it on. In the end, my boss just gave it to Marta to do. I can tell she's nervous about it, gearing herself up for the task.

'You want tea?' she asks me.

'What about your Coke?' I say.

She looks at the can as though unsure of how it got there.

I tell her that I'll make the tea if she likes.

She twirls a pen between two fingers, then tests the nib on the back of her hand. 'Sure, if you're offering,' she says, absently. 'If you're making one, I'll have tea.'

I fill the mugs from the water dispenser. Everyone here likes their tea very strong. I like that too, but I also put in a lot of milk. I show Marta her cup. 'Does that look about right?'

She nods and takes the mug from me.

'Do you know what you're going to say?' I ask.

'What can you write about something like that?' she says. 'What can you write about that on a form?'

'You can say what you saw,' I tell her. I don't really want to talk about it at all.

'Reasonable force, then,' she says. She is looking at me carefully. She wants me to tell her that would be okay.

'Is that what you saw?' I ask.

'I saw some people like us doing an impossible job,' she says. 'Dealing with impossible people.'

We both know that it wasn't *reasonable force* but it's not my job to make her feel bad. She's just doing the best she can. Her eyes are wide and bloodshot. She is sipping from her Diet Coke again. There's no way she can be sleeping properly. No one healthy looks like that.

My mum always told me that if you can do someone a kindness you should. Today, my kindness will be trying not to make Marta feel bad.

She turns to face the computer and pulls up the report document on the screen. 'Best get it over with I reckon,' she says.

More protesters are arriving for the demonstration. They're walking down the long gravel drive. The detention centre is a cut-off place and I wonder where it is they've left their cars. At the pet cemetery? At the activity centre down the road?

'It's like they know,' Marta says to me. 'They always pick the shittiest days.'

\*\*\*

My mum quit drinking in January. Now she looks after Jemima while I'm at work and I pay her for her time. It's not a bad arrangement for us, though my mum doesn't really like kids and Jemima is often bored. I haven't said anything about it because I like things as they are. This way, I get the best of her all the time. With me, Jemima is always inventing things – pictures, stories, clothes, new kinds of animals, planets, dance routines. When I look at her, I think she could invent the world over. She is pure magic. I think she could do whatever she wants.

Some of the women here are pregnant and some are very sick. There are others who are considered to be a danger to themselves. There are two women on suicide watch. Maybe one of them is genuinely mad. She doesn't speak to anyone, not to us and not to them, and from time to time she packs all her belongings into a pillowcase and carries them around with her wherever she goes. She hasn't tried to hurt herself for a while, but we've kept her on watch because her behaviour remains strange. Probably the pillowcase is a coping mechanism. I guess I'm glad she's got one of those.

There's a mental health nurse who comes in to talk to them sometimes. He also does training days with us. There are things called *sensitivity exercises* which are supposed to make us more aware of people's needs. Many of the women have a history of sexual abuse. Almost all of them have seen some terrible things. The fact is I don't want to be aware. Awareness is difficult for me. I have a lot of strategies for avoiding it, now. Some people say that knowledge is power, that information is valuable. Those people don't work in a place like this. I don't want the information because I still have to turn up every day.

\*\*\*

When I can't sleep I take Temazepam. The doctor was reluctant to prescribe it, at first. I refused his other suggestions – Sertraline, Citalopram, Amitriptyline, Doxepin. I told him I didn't want them because I know they can make you fat. Mum's been on Sertraline for six months now and already she's outgrown two pairs of jeans. It's not that she doesn't look good, she looks better than ever before, but I'm not willing to give up on my body. I had to work hard on it after Jemima was born. I like being the one who says no to the biscuit tin, who puts skimmed milk in her tea. I'm not an attractive woman, but that doesn't mean I have no pride.

Sometimes I wear lipstick at the weekends. Jemima loves it when I do. She likes to watch me apply it. She can look very serious sometimes. Once I asked her if she wanted to try the lipstick for herself. She frowned at me and shook her head.

'You're grown up,' she said. 'But I am still very small.' She tutted at me like I ought to have known this all along.

'You have a big personality,' I said. 'You're a big-small person, you know.'

Then she laughed and I went on putting on my lipstick and she went on looking at me, but smiling.

\*\*\*

The hunger strike began when a woman named Grace explained to everyone that they had to fight for their rights. With a plan of action and a set of specific demands, there was a chance they might be heard. They made a list. *For the attention of the Home Office,* they wrote. Some journalists began to take an interest. There was a social media campaign. One or two of the women here agreed to speak to radio presenters on the phone. That was when my boss began to feel uneasy. He told us not to take any shit. It seemed to him that we were being undermined, though of course it was never up to us to make the rules. I don't really know what he was worried about. You can't be undermined in a game that belongs to someone else.

When the women arrive here, they are often hopeful and defiant. They talk to their lawyers and to us about their cases all the time. When their families and friends come to visit, they make jokes and they often smile. In the beginning, it just seems like a bad dream. They can write it off as a terrible mistake. Over time, their personalities start to change. I guess one thing I've learned is that we're all made up, in some way, of the things we see. If all you see is a beige waiting room, a grey cafeteria and a barred window that only opens half an inch, eventually something changes inside of you. Your inner life becomes beige and grey as well.

Grace is a very good talker. She gets in all our heads. She has more education than all of us put together. It doesn't make things easy for her. Indefinite detention, she says, is *egregiously cruel*. I had to look up the word *egregiously*. Because she uses it so often I started to think it must mean something else.

My boss says Grace is manipulative, conniving, trouble-making. When I talked to him about it he said it was all very simple in his view. An end to indefinite detention would mean fewer of them, and fewer of them would mean fewer of us. He said that I had to be smart. *If you're smart, then you'll act in your own best interests.* That was what he said. I felt he was implying something else, something worse. *Don't you care about that kid of yours?*

\*\*\*

Marta finishes her report and slides it over the desk towards me. The protesters are chanting around the perimeter of the fence. *Women for refugee women*, they say. And then: *No woman is illegal to us*. From here, their voices are soft and harmonious, rumbling around like a hymn. If they hit the right frequency, I think, perhaps the walls will start to crumble. The bars on the windows will fall right out. I saw something like that happen once, on a TV show Jemima likes to watch. Some magical creatures hummed and all the bricks of a castle came tumbling down. When the princess ran free, Jemima clapped her hands for a long time.

'Can you read it over for me?' Marta says.

'I was there,' I say. 'I already know what happened.'

'I want to know what you think,' she says. She has drunk both the tea and the Diet Coke. Her legs are jiggling beneath the desk.

'I know what happened,' I say again.

'Please,' she says. 'Please. I want you to see what I've written down.'

*** 

When I was still quite small, I remember my mum telling me that a lot of the things we learned at school were wrong. 'They'll tell you that you're all born equal,' she said. 'It's a load of crap. Get it out of your head.' I can remember exactly where we were sitting when she said it. I was in her usual chair and she was in mine. She had given me a bowl of cereal to eat because she was going out. Her hair looked nice and she had colour on her cheeks. She was wearing a silky blouse with red spots. I told her she looked pretty and she nodded at me, sagely. 'That's one thing to our advantage,' she said. 'For now, we'll work with that.'

***

Marta's report begins with a basic outline. *Officer ____ made a comment implying that the hunger strikers would have healthier physiques if only they would agree to eat more food. Detainee number ____ interpreted this as an inappropriate sexual remark.*

When it comes to the fight, she has gone into a lot of detail. She explains how the situation escalated, how some of the officers got riled up. They called for back-up and some more DCOs turned up in riot gear. Some of the women lashed out. They made the first move. Their outburst was met with a disproportionate response from the officers. Things got way out of hand. Marta has listed a lot of the violent things they did. She has not written *reasonable force*.

I look over at her. She is tapping her nails frantically against the side of the empty drinks can. It makes a horrible, tinny empty sound, but she's in time with the singing outside. 'Do you think I'll get into trouble?' she says.

I shrug. 'I think you've explained what you saw.'

'And if he doesn't like it?'

'Then I suppose he'll give you some feedback.'

'You don't think he'll take me off the day shifts? "Flexible working hours" and all that?'

I tell her I don't know. There haven't been many incidents quite like this one. We don't know yet what he's expecting of us. Marta also has a little girl, older than Jemima, already in school.

She pulls a packet of cigarettes from her bag and shakes them at me. We walk down the stairs to the walled courtyard outside.

In natural light, her skin looks awful. Her mascara has powdered over her cheeks. 'Are you all right?' I ask.

She shakes her head and looks at the floor.

It's a long time since I've had a cigarette. It catches in my throat and after a few drags I feel queasy. I let it burn out while Marta smokes quickly and lights another as soon as she has finished the first.

The protesters are on the other side of the building. They have occupied the large grassy areas in front of the wire fences and the enormous security gates. I imagine myself standing among them, being jostled by their bodies, hearing their voices in the air beside my ears. I think about changing out of my uniform, putting on my jeans, and joining the back of the crowd. They'd never know that I work here, that I've seen first-hand all the things that they hate. I think about Grace and whether or not their singing is heartening to her. Perhaps she will feel vindicated, knowing that all these people are on her side.

I turn to Marta. 'You forgot about Grace,' I say. 'She's not in your report.'

'Grace wasn't there,' says Marta, surprised.

'She was still involved,' I say. I drop my cigarette on the floor and, even though it's already gone out, I crush it with the tip of my boot. Then I feel bad for leaving it there, so I pick it up and put it in the bin.

\*\*\*

My mum sometimes tells me that I've raised a precocious child.

'She's three,' I say. 'She's not raised. And what does precocious even mean?'

'You were never like that,' she says. 'You never had that attitude. Jemima thinks she can do whatever she wants.'

It isn't true, but I don't usually argue. She can think what she likes because I know the truth. Jemima is a thoughtful child. Maybe she talks a lot about the things she wants to be and do when she's older, but I encourage her to think like that, to know that everything is possible for her.

\*\*\*

Grace is a wheelchair user. She often gets left behind. Something happens during or after a mealtime and all the officers are called elsewhere. Because the centre isn't very accessible, she has to wait for us to help her get back downstairs. During the events of the day before yesterday, we were gone a long time. When the fight broke out, we were all called to the scene. Then it took a long while for things to calm down and we had to do head counts several times. By the time I realised Grace was missing she'd been in the cafeteria for three hours. She hadn't eaten anything of course, but she had taken some water and some coffee. Most of them still go to the cafeteria, just to get a change of scene. By the time I found her, she was cold and crying and there was a terrible smell because she had soiled herself.

'You people,' she said. Her voice was calm. In spite of her tears and the coldness of the room, she had perfect control over her speech. She looked at me directly. 'You're disgusting,' she said. 'I don't know how you sleep at night.'

\*\*\*

At five thirty when I finish my shift, the demonstration is still going strong. They are still singing, still chanting, waving their colourful banners in the air. I know Jemima won't mind too much if I'm late because it happens quite a lot. I also know that it's time for a change. I want to make her proud of me but I'm afraid of something I can't yet name. It's a big-small feeling, quiet but strong, and buried deep down. Like the voices she hears in the furniture, it's something impossible that can't get out.

JOSEPH ALLEN BOONE

# The Sound of Water

You stand watching from the edge of the jacuzzi as he lowers himself into the steaming water, as he yields to the hissing cauldron. Face turned skywards to the October moon, arms flung askew, he sinks beneath the churning surface holding his breath. Eyes closed; lips curved in ecstasy; smile visible despite the ripples breaking his image into a hundred refractions, pink against turquoise.

That sound as he went under, was it a gurgle of delight or the hum of the jets tumbling the waters? You wonder, knowing what you now know about the boy, studying his slender body, pale as moonlight in the underwater light, as he lazily sinks to the bottom, opens his mouth to expel a trail of bubbles, arms swaying like sea plants whispering their private language. Suddenly he springs upwards, bursting into the night air as forcefully as the spray of a Bernini fountain, eyes flashing and face beaming in the cloud of steam that hovers above the tub.

*Little fishies, my little fishies*: those were the words, you recall, that Tiberius used to describe the wantons who frolicked in the baths of his pleasure palace on Capri. Once the jaded emperor tired of his minions, he casually tossed them off the island's perilous cliffs, their lithesome bodies shattering against the rocks jutting from the surf below.

My little fishie, you want to say to him. I'll never hurt you.

But you know he won't hear.

\*\*\*

You remember the first moment you saw him, that July evening when the heat wave nearly paralyzed the city. You opened the front door and there he stood in the cold rush of the air-conditioning, dark liquid eyes at once expectant and hesitant. Before you could invite him into your glass and steel house, perched high on the hills overlooking Los Angeles, his hand darted to his mouth, then he tapped his ears—all this as he shrugged his shoulders with a crooked smile. A split second of surprise, even panic, flashed across your face as you grasped the situation. When it came to masseurs, you thought you'd seen it all. But this was new: he was deaf, he

56

was mute. Your momentary panic made you blush; you felt pity for his affliction; you felt, oddly, an arousal of interest.

\*\*\*

That was the beginning.

The third time you hired him, in August, he revealed via the BuzzCard app on his iPhone that his name was David. No surprise there—you'd assumed that "Lance"—the name in his online advertisement for massage-plus services—was an alias. They usually were. He was Mexican-American, an achingly beautiful young man who, once stripped to his black Calvin Kleins, looked a full decade younger than his already young twenty-six years. His calves and legs were as impressive, and as furry, as those of a triathalon athlete, but his chest and arms as spindly and as hairless as an adolescent's, begging (so you wanted to believe) to be hugged, protected. Despite such bony arms he was amazingly strong; all to the good since you'd hired him (so you told yourself) to work the knots out of your back. He seemed genuinely to like you, though you were more than twice his age, your hairline receding, body starting to slacken, and too many white chest hairs to bother plucking out the recalcitrant offenders anymore.

How did he cope, you wondered during that first meeting: cope with being deaf and mute and gay? With being deaf and mute and gay and doing *this* for a livelihood? Did any clients, flustered at his inability to speak, turn him away on sight? You wanted to ask all these questions and more, but they felt too complex to condense into the Buzzword texts he and you used to communicate. ASL? David shrugged. He'd learned the rudiments, he told you, but with his family he had developed his own language of signs, plus he read lips fairly well, and nowadays he mostly used his iPhone to communicate, he could peck out messages as swiftly in English as in Spanish: ah, nimble fingers of youth, you think. The same fingers that seemed to feel nothing odd, nothing shameful, in touching your naked body, telegraphing your desire back to you in the orgasmic dribs and drabs that at the conclusion of the massage were the best you could muster—but for which pleasures you were, at the end of the day, grateful.

Most of all you wanted to ask how he had come to be so well-adjusted, so *normal* in spite of the difficulties of growing up deaf and gay and Latino in America—for that was what David radiated, more than any other quality; an almost irritatingly wholesome normality; as if he were just *any* youth barely out of his teens, vague about his future but filled

57

with self-confidence and dozens of friends, a youth who claimed to live on a shoestring budget but was somehow able to afford vacations back home to Texas or New York or Europe, a youth on intimate terms with parents and siblings—they're fine that I'm gay, he tells you, they've known forever. But do they know what you *do* for a living, you wonder; what did you tell them when you took off for Budapest last spring? Some of his background you know because David's told you; some you've learned by tracking his Facebook posts. But you crave to know more. You rue your incapacity to plumb his silent inner world. Whence this craving? Why do you care?

What you *do* know, after several weeks, is that water is his element. On his Instagram account you've seen the photos of him mugging on countless beaches: Santa Monica and Venice of course, but also Oahu, Puerto Vallarta, Sitges. And at indoor pools; the great baths of Budapest. When he takes a shower in your bathroom after finishing the massage, he often doesn't emerge for half an hour, the steam doesn't dissipate for another thirty minutes. Once he discovered that you had a jacuzzi on the deck, he started inviting himself over to relax in the heated water while the city below shimmered like a mirage in the mist rising from the foam.

You, of course, have been more than happy to oblige: your version of offering a happy ending. Sometimes, when he's finally had enough of the heat, has lifted himself to the edge of the tub and lies back on his towel with only his knees dangling in the water, you've paddled up between those muscled limbs—such a contrast to his thin chest—and, as you've propped your elbows on his pelvis, he's let you play with his penis, languid, soft, then slightly turgid, you've kissed his inner thighs, massaged his downy calves, and when he falls asleep your heart is ready to burst.

\*\*\*

One evening David explains that under water he feels as if he is no longer deaf; water speaks to him; its rippling movements communicate; his floating limbs sound in the shallows and depths, his body hums with intimations of what it might be like, in the world above water, to hear.

You think: not to know the timbre of a bird's warble, or the evening rustle of crickets, or the thrashing of branches in a gust of wind—what would such a world be like? You try but fail to imagine the universal silence. Can David conjure the crash of a door slamming? a chapel bell ringing? the whoosh of a fart, expelled?

***

You've known him two months, hired him for a half-dozen massages, when you happen upon his escort ad. Not on Massage Finder, your go-to site, but Rent Boys, which you only skim once in a blue moon. David's photograph stares out at you, the same beatific face you've come to know up close. It's the identical headshot he uses on Massage Finder—but here it is followed by a parade of sexually explicit nude photographs, gleefully whorish poses, the naughty leer of his dark eyes daring the viewer to beg for more.

You are surprised; taken aback, perturbed; perhaps even a bit betrayed. You thought you'd started to understand the way he balanced his world of normalcy, of family and friends, with a profession that pushed the limits of respectability—after all, you told yourself, what gay masseur in Los Angeles, professional or otherwise, doesn't include a bit of sensuality as part of his services these days? But the thought of David overtly escorting—the web site showed he had been actively posting his services for three years—adds an indeterminate note to the portrait you've composed in your mind: he's selling his body brazenly, not a qualm in the world. Yet he's not desperate; not jaded; neither calculating nor conniving; there is no whiff of the hustle that you've encountered in the handful of male escorts you've hired in your lifetime, nothing furtive. An open face, genuine smile, hopeful eyes: that is your image of David, the little fishie, little minnow, who likes to float in your hot tub, his limbs fanning out like sea plants as he absorbs the sounds of water in silent glee. That is the image of the boy you've wished into being.

Not the escort whose list of services glare from the computer screen: *Open to all kink, dom/sub, mild/wild, role playing, pushing the limits.* Plus: *Great international travel companion.*

David, you wondered. Who *are* you, David?

Who am I?

***

The next time he appears at your door, you scan his face for a clue, a talisman you might have missed. Yet David looks more boyishly innocent than ever: *carefree*, that's the aura he always emanates, carefree and impish in a manner without guile. But you find yourself worrying about him, about this very guilelessness—does he always enter strangers' homes so trustingly as he had yours, so lacking in caution? You fret—you knew that all escorts, all masseurs, faced potential risk when they made outcalls to unknown clients; but what special dangers might befall a youth like David, so slight in build and unable to utter a word—much less a "safe word" during the rough sex that seemed part of his repertoire? Can he signal that enough is enough? Or is enough never enough? Does his inability to speak add to the thrill for his johns; does the uncertainty, the risk, add to the pleasure for David?

As you usher David, dressed in shiny blue gym pants trimmed in white, inside, you flash on Coach Roper's phys ed class. You were a high school sophomore; the Dark Ages for kids of David's generation. Roper's reputation for cruelty preceded him. But particularly abusive was his means of teaching the class to box. Once your right hand was mitted with a glove, he tied your left hand to that of your opponent, then blindfolded you both. Your mandate was to pummel each other until one of you dropped. The victor's reward? To help his fallen companion limp to the locker-room showers, sluice the bloody traces of triumph off the loser's body. You'd been lashed to Billy, the perfect scholar-athlete you (and a great deal of the rest of the school) idolized—a schoolboy crush before you understood the nature of your crushes—and he'd soundly walloped you, blows to the the rib cage bringing you to the point of girlish tears. And when, alone together in the showers, he'd lathed the soapy water over you as blood from a split lip trickled down your chin and dripped into the white foam, you'd gotten hard and had to turn away. But for the next two weeks, you revered the purple bruise on your left rib cage—tracery of an erotic awakening as you begin to lust for all the Billys of the world.

David precedes you down the hallway, reaching behind to grab your hand and tug you in his wake as he leads the way to the bedroom. Beyond the glass walls, the lights of the city float below. You're in heaven. David's step across the bedroom carpeting is light, almost a skip; a prance; a dance; and you can't resist the impulse to reach forward with your free hand to slap his firm ass through his skin-tight jeans: loud *whack!* that you—only you—hear. He glances over his shoulder at you, a look of startlement, a smile of frisky delight. Later, when you flip onto your back, your head hanging over the mattress's edge as orgasm ripples your limbs, David reaches forward and swats your face, hard enough to sting. He tugs on your penis with a quickened pace as a glint shows in his eye—even in the candlelit dark you see the glint, the mirth—and then he slaps your face again and again, a thunder of blows till you see stars, smack-smack-smacks that cease only when you finally shove his hand away. No: in your version of sign: no.

Something new, unspoken but not unacknowledged, enters your encounters. There's the time you spontaneously sit up mid-massage and pull him over your knee as you yank down his Calvins, slapping his ass cheeks to a crimson flush; he moans sounds as close to speech as you've ever heard him utter as he curves his ass upwards to meet your palm. There's the time he pushes his forearm across your throat, elbow cutting deep into your thorax as you are about to shoot, you black out. And the time showering together when you feel another hot stream spraying your leg, its arc rising as he grows hard. Neither of you make mention of these moments afterwards; you go about your normal routines, getting dressed, exchange of money, a bit of Buzz Word banter about weekend plans, before he leaves, off to meet friends at a new club on the Strip or in Echo Park. Always friends; his life spread across the face of the city.

\*\*\*

August: the traditional vacation month for your tribe. But from the opening of your psychiatric practice, you insisted that September would be your chosen month of solitude, your respite from the dark vortex of your patients' inner anguish. Then you'd travel abroad, go anywhere that struck your fancy—almost always allotting one week in London to see as much theatre as seven days allowed. Was it really a decade ago that you saw Stoppard's *Invention of Love* at the Royal National? You'd chuckled when the mythic Charon, exasperated at the recently deceased A. E. Housman's incessant chatter, asks his passenger if he can just be quiet for a moment and Housman mordantly replies: *Yes, I expect so. My life was marked by long silences.* For all his verbal wit, silence had resonated throughout the Victorian poet-scholar's life—product of the unrequited gay desires he kept closeted to the end. You, in contrast, child of the Seventies, came out in med school, perhaps not the flaming rocket that Wilde in the afterlife admonishes Housman for not having been—but you'd made a statement, yes in your own way you'd been brave. Nonetheless your spine tingled with a flash of recognition, a feeling of loneliness and inadequacy that had never entirely faded, when the actor spoke those pregnant words. So, too, in your life: so much left unspoken, so much brooding silence, a listener rather than talker by profession, stalled midstream in a limbo of your own choosing.

It's already mid-September, mid-vacation, but you feel too restive to leave home—oddly reluctant to travel, to commit to a plan. Now, listening to the sounds of David splashing in your hot tub, under a starlit night, watching him sink lazily beneath the foaming surface, his hands swaying in their private language, you wonder: why is this bafflement? what do you need to hear spoken to fill this void?

\*\*\*

You fantasize taking David to the Gulf of Mexico, showing him the secluded beach on the spit of turf off Dauphin Isle where your family used to vacation. Alternating streams of emerald and aquamarine hue marked its transparent waters, you remember watching the shells waft back and forth on the sandy bottom by your toes. The waves were gentle, little crests slapping you lazily across the face, more salty tickle than a slap; but the undertow was sometimes unexpectedly forceful—and once (you were nine) you were tugged under, the solid world slipping away as you found yourself flailing in deepening waters. But your father had seen and swum out, he'd wrested you from Neptune's muscular vice with his even stronger iron grip.

"I wasn't in trouble!"

So you protested.

"Don't lie to me, my little minnow." Your father held you by your thin shoulders and fixed your gaze sternly. "You almost drowned. As sure as I'm looking at a very scared boy."

Would David go with you? He might, after all he loves travel—and you certainly wouldn't be the only older man to seek out his company on a vacation for the right price. But would the homely backwaters of your youth, your long bygone youth, be enticing enough for so worldly a traveler as David? You want to offer a glimpse of your past to David—what if he doesn't care? Is that what you are afraid of? Why not take the risk—what's lost by asking? You've more than earned a trip, even if it's not Europe this time round.

So, as if in a dream, you find yourself back in Alabama, driving a rented car from Mobile to the shore, where you will hire a motorboat to carry the two of you across the bay to Dauphin Isle. You imagine the surprise David is sure to display when the gulf currents enfold his eager body in their embrace. Only the two of you, in the hidden cove you discovered as a teenager, far away from the main beach, basking on towels spread over glistening white sand.

You watch as David stands, his eyes darting right and left mischievously before he unties his floppy surfer trunks, lets them fall to his feet as he preens in the sun, autumnal breeze ruffling his dark shock of hair. He shrugs with a smile that says volumes—or nothing—and lies back down, closing his eyes in satisfaction. Who is there to see? Who but you to admire the pearly whiteness that runs from his hairless navel down his thighs, stopping at his kneecaps? You want to swoon: the sun is exploding prisms in your head.

Then you find yourself in the water with David.

The voice of the mild surf is seductive, it invites you to lose yourself in its mazes. You and David float together, suspended in aquamarine depths, he suddenly throws his arms around you, holding tightly, in turn you squeeze him tightly, flesh hard against flesh. He looks into your eyes, abysses of solitude open in his molten pupils as they meet yours, and his gaze throws out a challenge, a dare. Answering in his silent language, you accept, and the two of you wrestle, playfully but aggressively, each holding the other more and more tightly as the water funnels you downwards, your bodies a rotating vortex. Your legs fan out in the currents, you perform an intimate pas de deux as you sink, pirouetting in the downward spiral, each of you wrestling for ascendancy.

It could be the hot tub in your backyard. A beach on Oahu. Anywhere.

Underwater, you open your eyes and he is still staring at you, smiling, daring you to see how long you can hold out. You are both struggling now. He won't let go. You can't stay under much longer, your lungs are bursting.

You listen to the water jets spraying out their thunder. Hot steam is rising somewhere, rising above the rippling surface that breaks the black sky into fragments.

The water speaks with its touch. David speaks with his touch, his vice-like grip, refusing to release you.

The emerald eddies, flowing in and out with your breath, are filling you with liquid music, the ocean's undertow sounding a vibrant counterpoint to David's melody. His limbs are singing to you, and the pressure in your lungs is unbearable.

You give in, exhale as a thousand bubbles rush out and inhale as the bitter salt of the sea rushes in. You listen to the murmuring currents, the bass profundo of the Gulf, the symphony of sounds exploding your brain as he pulls you under, sinking, his ecstatic smile mirrored on your face.

***

You are not there to see David spring from the bubbling froth—erect as the spray of a Bernini fountain and gulping in gasps of oxygen with the vigor of the newly born, the resurrected—spring out of the steamy mist of the roiling waters and into the colder, sharper rush of the October air.

# Bedded

Late in October our Margery went to bed. Some people whispered that she had given up on the village after the opening of the militia question, but most of us thought she had just finally succumbed. This was understandable. Her bed was tall and high and its wooden headrest was carved with the fall, apples outstretched, hands waiting, snakes in greenery. The bed was deep and layered: straw in the box, which made the room smell like earth and sun, a thin mattress top, then the feather mattress. Then sheets, warm cotton, soft like worn t-shirts, and Margery slipped in here. Over her more sheets, smoothing her in close; they didn't match, off shades of green above and below. A quilt, deep and soft as snowfall, heaped over her. Its cover was white pin-pricked with stars in flashes of grey and yellow. Another blanket over that, a thin grey layer of felt. The coverlet at the top, red and green, curling tapestry, quilted stitches, golden embroidery threaded over it so that it was rough to the touch and scratched your palm. Margery, hidden safe deep below it, had nothing to fear. She had four pillows, two fat and two thin, and another long one which she tucked between her knees on the nights her back ached. These were white and pale grey, their pillowcases yellowing. She had two small cushions in the same red and gold as the coverlet, and she used these when she wanted to sit up, nestled into the hollow of her back, or hugged them to her chest when she required company.

Margery's bedroom was well-stocked. On either side of the bed books towered high, all the many books she had spent the twenty-eight years of her life not reading, not once or not enough. A hefty hardback *Magic Mountain* supporting Toni Morrison paperbacks, Alice Munro short stories propped against Elaine Scarry and Eve Kosofky Sedgwick, the stalwart thick editions of Dickens and Dumas and Dostoevsky forming firm bases for luridly coloured paperbacks by newly forgotten writers, recipe books heavy on scene setting, thin children's classics, poetry.

Fenced in by the books, or held awkwardly just out of reach beyond them, was the rest of Margery's larder: cold boxes filled with salami and longer lasting cheeses, sticks of Peperami, vacuum sealed pork pies, bags of bread stuffed with enough preservatives to keep them fresh for some weeks, ring-pull tins of baked beans and dull teaspoons clattering beside them, jars of peanut butter and Nutella, a couple of bottles of whiskey and cheap rosé, Pot Noodles and Cup-a-Soups and boxes of Yorkshire teabags next to a kettle plugged in with an extension cord. Several barrels of water. She stuffed packets of dried fruit and nuts into the spaces in the headboard, tucked here and there under a curl of wood, so like a squirrel she wouldn't have to reach far. Then, just the usual things that might come up now and again. A torch, extra batteries, a vibrator, packs of playing cards, hot water bottles, a 12 pound dumbbell. Her Moon Cup.

For all that, though, when Margery went to bed she didn't read or play or eat, or if she did any of that, she did it in secret. From what we saw when we peered in her bedroom window which peeked out onto an alley just off the High Street or slipped over the warm floorboards of her house to make sure the fireplace in her room was stoked and that her sour breath came regularly, Margery went to bed and slept. She pulled the blankets up high over her head and tucked herself down and went away from us. She dozed nineteen or twenty hours a day, her eyelashes fluttering against her cheek, her breathing slow and deep. All we could see was the red-gold slip of her hair, the colour of the pale autumn harvest that was passing through and away, and a slice of frowning eyebrow. Mrs. Gardiner, who aired out Margery's bedroom on the rare sunny mornings, once announced that Margery had turned in her sleep, the blankets pooling around her chin, and revealed a mouth sulky and lax as a toddler's, pink lips parted. Mrs. Gardiner patted a cool hand against Margery's cheek to be sure all was well and told us with pleasure that Margery had been flushed but not feverish. She had looked perfectly comfortable, Mrs. Gardiner said, and added wistfully that maybe it was time for her own nap.

Margery slept through Halloween, though only a few children happened to knock on her door; Margery was kind to the village children and they loved her devotedly in turn, and most were mindful of her sleep. She slept through Bonfire Night, when we all went to the Green and stood warming ourselves against the flames and pretending not to notice the teenagers getting drunk in the hedges. When the parish council resumed halfway through November, there was talk of waking her to update her on the first discussions around the militia issue, but after all Margery had been covering the story for the local paper and knew what we were due to discuss. We decided to let her be.

Snow came in December, earlier than it had been for years. On the first Sunday of the Advent, Reverend Pickering spoke to us about the quiet tenderness of the season and reminded us to be kind to one another, to use these weeks to bring the year to a gentle and thoughtful end. We were making important decisions, he told us, and though perhaps the councillors looked particularly important the whole church nodded, happily bobbing heads in unison.

The Reverend closed with Psalm 63, David lost in the wilderness, which should have worried us, but he lingered on its loving notes. *My soul will be satisfied as with fat and rich food, and my mouth will praise you with joyful lips, when I remember you upon my bed,* he said in his clear, warm voice, *and meditate on you in the watches of the night,* and we all looked out the eastern windows of the church, where, down and off the High Street, Margery slept on. At the end of the service, the Reverend told us that the ladies of the Women's Institute were looking for volunteers with chainsaws to assist in the Village Beautification Initiative and help them remove the dead trees near the graveyard, that Mr. Beachworth was in the Royal Sussex County Hospital again but with God's grace he would be home before Christmas, and that Margery was still sleeping well and people were reminded to keep their voices low as they walked past her window.

Later that week, Emma Rugg announced that she had a seasonal job in the big M&S in Brighton. Everyone wondered what she'd do with young Tom, who had reacted poorly to daycare and was too young for kindergarten, and then she disappeared with no word. It wasn't until a few of the ladies from Kensington Road passed Margery's window that it was reported Tom was there, ensconced in Margery's bed, with a puzzle. Margery's head had been turned towards him on her pillow. No one could see if her eyes were open.

We were all shocked and declared it a great shame at first, both for Margery's sake and young Tom's, who after all had a hard enough time what with feckless Emma as his mother and takeaway for dinner most nights and no father figure to speak of, but after some time we had to begrudgingly give it up. Emma was cheerful and much less sullen when she could work, even made some friends down in Brighton who came back and helped decorate her house. Tom reported with great authority that Margery's bed was the most comfortable in the village, and that she was kind and let him bring his colouring and eat bubblegum that she kept stashed under the bed. Margery herself barely spoke, but she seemed to stir when Tom was there, watching him from under heavy, sleep-gritted eyelashes. Late at night, Emma Rugg let herself into the little cottage to pick Tom up and often found him fast asleep and nuzzled into Margery's arms, heavy toddler limbs twined around Margery's neck, Margery's slim, wasting arm slung over him. Emma whispered thank you very much and eased Tom out of Margery's hold, and sometimes Margery would push up on her elbows and manage a sleepy goodnight as Emma carried Tom back out into the cool night and home.

After that quite a few children took to coming round to Margery's house, when they were restless or lonely or if there had been some playground war that required all sides to skulk away and nurse sore pride. They climbed in and out of Margery's bed and Margery let them, did not mind the muddy footprints on her coverlet. She did not interact with them much, but she shared her books and her food and some of the little ones were allowed to brush her hair. Which had gone thin and dull, then greasy, then suddenly swollen into health, like a fattened animal tucked away in its den.

We talked, now and then, of sending Dr. Hammond to examine her, but he said himself that it was not as though Margery was sick. She had announced her intention to go to bed one Friday afternoon, at the newspaper offices, when the small staff were pushing her to join them for drinks at the pub that evening. 'No,' she said. 'I'm going to sleep all weekend.' She might have been trying to break it to us gently, so that when the weekend extended itself indefinitely we were not hurt. Her colleagues thought it was fair enough; Margery had worked harder than anyone, and she was exhausted. She stayed up very late, listening to the radio reports and combing through the social media that the rest of us avoided. She still had London habits from her time away, she drank large amounts of black coffee, she worked out regularly, she asked Reverend Pickering if he had time for a 'quick catch up' and then quizzed him relentlessly about his official role, her thick eyebrows drawn together and frowning. We suspected that Reverend Pickering was a little relieved that Margery had left off bothering him for a while, and no one, especially Dr. Hammond, could deny that the rest was good for her.

Sleep looked very appealing on Margery. Her breath came even and regular, her body relaxed deep into the layers of her bed. Tiny, strange spots scattered across her cheeks for a few days, puzzling us until Mrs. Gardiner declared that they were milk spots, the same ones newborns got. They melted back into Margery's skin, so clear and warm now, not even the faintest touch of shadows under her eyes and the new crows' feet smoothing out again. Her face looked like a puddle of cream and we wanted to dabble our fingers in it.

After the children spent time with her they started to sleep more, troublesome toddlers making it all the way through the night, five year olds eschewing their usual dawn awakening to let the whole house sleep late on Saturdays. The rest of us picked up on it, too. Our old people were most talented and could go to bed for three to four days, drifting in and out of drowsy warmth, coming out fresh-faced on Sunday with their cheeks pink and their eyes bright; and the teenagers, too, lasted a long while, and did not bother to stir on Sundays. But most of us struggled to stay abed long, roused by bladders, anxiety, restless leg syndrome. We had the new council meetings to keep us occupied during the days and at night we could not help thinking about them, running them over in our heads. Sometimes we went to Margery's bed for inspiration, stopping by on our ways home in the evening as though her simple rest could inspire or infect us, but after a few of us started patting timidly at the pointed shape of Margery's feet under the covers, Reverend Pickering advised us to stop. He said, smiling, that there was no need for us to be so fenian about things, and that we did not need Margery's intervention, only a clear conscience and a long day's useful labour.

At the time Reverend Pickering was considered a good judge, as he was being so sensible and practical about the militias. When the village hall flooded in the first dreary December downpour, Reverend Pickering offered up the vestry for our discussions until the tidemarks and sodden leaves could be dealt with, and even when the hall was serviceable again we preferred to stay in the vestry. It was small and warm, and Mrs. Taylor with some of the other ladies from the Women's Institute kept an eye on things and popped in with tea and biscuits, unlike Angelina, the assistant to the parish clerk, who only brought lukewarm coffee, and was sulky whenever we called her away from her computer.

The discussions were meant to cover a wide range of concerns: economic, geographical, communal, but they degenerated mostly into conversations about whether or not we could trust Hastings. Mr. Gardiner, who was elected chairman that year, believed that we could; what was more, he said, with their influx of Londoners, Hastings had more resources and money and we would be stronger together. Reverend Pickering took up the leading voice for the opposition, saying in his mild way that though Hastings was a lovely town and he had some friends there, it was better for our village to be self-sufficient. Forming our own militia would allow us greater control and protection over our own people, and though it seemed unlikely the militia would ever have to play a large role in the governance of our village and the great world outside it, he still believed it was better to be certain that we knew where we stood. Look at Yorkshire, after all, he said, and we reached for our next biscuits and agreed that Yorkshire was a great shame.

We spent many hours running over these same ideas, but we were never bored; we felt the nuances of the situation would be made clear the more we talked them through, and we were mindful that patience was a virtue and there was no great urgency, or at least not one that would be worth making a hasty, reckless decision. If possible, we wanted a unanimous decision, and indeed people changed their minds, flitting first one way and then the other in a way that gave us hope that no one was arguing merely because they could not bear to admit they had been wrong. Over the grey December weeks, it became clear that the eventual win would probably be for Reverend Pickering and his followers, and even Mr. Gardiner, though he did not give up his own side, seemed to acknowledge this in some way and only wanted to make sure we thought it through. He bore no ill-will to the Reverend, although he was unimpressed one Sunday after the Reverend dwelled on Paul's Epistle to the Ephesians.

'It calls for unity,' Reverend Pickering said, smiling out at us. 'Paul tells us that God has raised us *together*, and made us sit *together* in heavenly places in Christ Jesus. We are not alone, we are together. Now therefore, Paul says, ye are no more strangers and foreigners, but fellow citizens with the saints, and of the household of God. And we must stay together, and strive against our enemies, so that when the day of evil comes, we may be able to hold the sword of the Spirit, which is the word of God. Amen.'

'Amen,' we said.

'Bit on the nose,' Mr. Gardiner could be heard to grumble.

'Ah, but the Reverend knows what he's talking about,' Mrs. Gardiner said, and went to take her armful of flowers to Margery's room. She would spend the rest of the morning there, rearranging the vases and tidying up the empty wrappers and plastic around Margery's bed, moving quietly and humming a lullaby. Sometimes she cleaned the windows, so even as the winter closed us into its inexorable trap Margery's room still seemed filled with light and air, a grey, translucent veil that slipped over the woman in the bed and touched everything with soft, tentative hands.

On Christmas Eve the carollers sang outside Margery's window and, in the low glow of her fireplace and the candles someone had lit, she could be seen to roll to the side, groaning, her back hunched like a snail against us, one arm flung up over her head. In his Christmas sermon, Reverend Pickering reminded us that after all, Psalm 149 did not tell us to sing to the saints but that the saints themselves were joyful in glory, and sang aloud upon their beds. Perhaps we should be listening to Margery instead, he said, chuckling to himself, but when one or two of us bent our faces close to Margery's, there was no tune, only the curdled fog of her breath. Her lips parted enough that we could see white fuzz clinging to her tongue, and we worried, a little, that she was going further away from us.

We were miserable that January, feeling ourselves abandoned. The daylight scrunched in on itself, the decorations were pulled down and the streets looked bare and lost without them. The council talks stalled and then moseyed along, everyone stubborn and truculent, until we surprised ourselves by voting unanimously and all at once to form our own militia. The news, announced the next day by Reverend Pickering after his sermon, was met by astonishment and then a relieved surge of activity. The Women's Institute announced they would hold a fête to fundraise for supply and armament. They swept through the streets to collect jumble items, ascending like broad-shouldered, open-armed angels with curling hair and stern bosoms to ferret out each last volunteer and dusty jar of jam. Everyone could donate something, and everyone should; it was all for such a good cause, and indeed the only thing more important than giving everything away was buying it all up again on Saturday.

The Women's Institute were well-pleased with themselves, benevolent and gracious to the village. When the day of the fête came, cold but clear, the Green decked out with bunting and the rented trestle tables festive with their tablecloths, we agreed that they had done a wonderful job: everything bright and enticing, catching light where there was none, more than enough of Mrs. Taylor's most beloved jam and plenty of everyone else's, the games cheery and waiting. Reverend Pickering stood in perfect accord with Mr. Gardiner as they discussed this week's rainfall, and the whole village was polished to its very best.

And at the far end of the Green, first prize in the raffle and held aloft like a triumphant flag, was Margery's coverlet, the red, green and gold of it somehow holier than anything else there, more than the Reverend's collar, more than the familiar steeple rising above the Green. It looked alien. It looked beautiful. When we touched it, with the nervous feeling we were about to be chased away, it seemed to be even rougher to the touch, snarling and snagging at our fingers like a garden of thorns. We all wanted it very badly.

The day gambolled along, with regular intervals for the judging of the baking competition and Morris dancing. At the end of the day Reverend Pickering and Mrs. Taylor representing the Women's Institute announced that the fête had already raised a grand total of over £5,000 and everyone cheered. The raffle was drawn. Margery's blanket went to Emma Rugg, who stepped forward, her face astounded and slapped blank with joy, while Mrs. Gardiner slipped away to cry behind the bunting.

As it grew dark, everyone spilled into the pub to keep celebrating and drinking, heavy glasses of ale and rubied crystal, and Tom the landlord had to start serving wine in water glasses, there was so much demand, but a few of us worried about Margery. We thought she might be cold, without her coverlet; we thought it was too grand a gift. We slipped down High Street and to her window, and some of us announced our intention to fetch spare quilts or sleeping bags, but when we reached Margery's little house we saw there was no need. Margery's window was open to the winter-biter wind and she lay untouched by it. She was cosseted under heaped furs, coruscating red and brown in the earthen firelight. They swaddled her up to her chin. Once or twice she shifted, her throat bright with sweat. Mink, someone said, their voice low and uncertain, and someone else cleared their throat and said surely it was sable, and someone else, with a sound like the surf grating over rocks, said no, it was fox, look at the gleam of it. But we were all of us worried they were from something bigger.

The fête's successful fundraising meant that the week saw shipments of crates and stern men in suits with legal documents, and then we started signing everyone up, the young men boisterous and excitable, the older ones satisfied that a consensus had been reached. They looked terrible and joyful, and we felt suddenly sure that we had made the right decision.

There was a Women's Corps, too, who drilled on alternate afternoons. Some of us wondered if perhaps Margery would have joined them. When she first returned to the village, and most of us hadn't seen her in ten years and her parents were dead in that terrible crash and now her grandmother too, she had joined everything, with a hungry kind of loneliness. She had gone to the Women's Institute meetings, where she was the youngest by a generation, and to the Darts Club, her cracked leather jacket an odd fit with the rest of the boys. She had seemed genuinely regretful when she told Reverend Pickering that she couldn't help out with the Sunday School, that it was not, and she paused and her mouth quirked, not her bag. But if we were honest with ourselves, we knew she would not have been interested in the militia. By the time she took up the job as senior editor at the newspaper, under the doddering Alistair Warwick, she had already stopped going to most meetings. She ate alone, Sunday lunch at the pub with a book propped in front of her plate, and she went on long, solitary walks over the green hills and trails. She worked hard and kept to herself, though she was perfectly friendly, so no one turned against her. But when we met these days to talk about her now and again over a pint, or when a conversation in a corner wandered in unexpected directions, we remembered other things, like the low incredulity in her voice when we first began to discuss the militia, or the way her shoulders hunched higher, her back always turning on us. With the new lines beside her eyes she had looked the spit of her grandmother, which should have been a comfort and was not. Still, the lines were fading and spring was coming; we had hope that Margery would come back and see how brave we had been, after all.

Through the February drift the village seemed busier and brighter than the height of summer. Men marched in straight rows up and down the street and yelped with laughter like well-heeled dogs at each other's marksmanship. Mist curled around their ankles, lapped at their collars. Reverend Pickering stood smiling at the gate of the churchyard and nodded at each of them as they went past and Mr. Gardiner leaned out of the column to laugh and say, well, Reverend, you had it your way in the end, and perhaps that was no bad thing. There were ugly bruits from Hastings way but that, Reverend Pickering said, was to be expected.

The men passed under Margery's window. We had grown less careful of her quiet, as Margery seemed to sleep well no matter the riot, and the stragglers or those who grew winded or those who needed a fag break would stop and rest by her door. Some of the younger boys whistled through her window, but Mr. Gardiner came back to cuff them around the back of the neck and drag them on. Margery stirred and shifted, frowning. In the weak sunlight sometimes she grew too hot under the furs and threw them back, and we saw the long curve of her arm drooping with skin that had once been muscle. Her shirt slipped down her shoulders and there were twisting curls of black pelt in her armpits and her bed was littered with crumbs. Once the sheets had been changed but not anymore. She lay in yellowing sweat and the hay crackled underneath with the tiny stirrings of small animals finding new beds.

Mrs. Gardiner brought in bundles of dried lavender and tucked them under Margery's pillows, and Emma Rugg still dropped young Tom by to comb Margery's hair. We brought her church newsletters and the last smuggled dailies that made it from London; we thought that spring was coming, and the decision had been made, and Margery's rest might soon be complete, and when it was, Margery, who had always been bright and engaged before she gave up on us, would want to know all that she had missed.

It was only two or three days into March that we stepped into her room and heard our footsteps ring out like the sharp cracks of the boys taking potshots. The warm wooden floorboards of her room had all been pulled up and to our surprise, underneath were hyperborean flagstones, very ancient and regular and cold. They ringed around her bed, and under it, as close as we could see. We crawled across the room on hands and knees, our noses bent to stone. When her furs brushed our cheeks we looked about and saw that the newspapers had been left in untidy stacks and what was on top of them was much older. Illuminated manuscripts, their flexing animal bindings open so we saw trailing Latin and bright red and green illustrations of men riding snails, square-faced lions, women curled in loops and apostrophes. There was one beside Margery in the bed, too, but its cover was closed and her hand lay flat and possessive on it. We crawled away.

Reverend Pickering laughed from his pulpit and told us the story of Christ in the Garden of Gethsemane: earlier, earlier than you are thinking, he said, before the tragedy of our Saviour has come to bear, when He wanders in the garden and prays to His Father and returns to find His disciples sleeping, unable to sit through the night with Him; and He rebukes them; and He returns and finds them asleep again, and leaves to pray, and returns once more to say, Sleep on now, and take your rest: behold, the hour is at hand. Well, if Jesus could understand, Reverend Pickering said, and laughed again, though the next week when the first primroses came peeping and the Green was littered with crocuses, he was seen to be frowning. He changed the route of the drills so that the men marched by Margery's window three times a day. They sang now, because it had been found to warm their spirits on the cold nights when they sat up waiting, and it was easier to believe that there was no great and terrible reason for the song if they sang during the days, too. But Margery slept on.

The room stayed chilly, despite the fire and the furs; the cold, hard stone radiated outwards. Mrs. Gardiner wore her winter coat through the brightening days and stopped attending meetings for the Village Beautification Initiative. On the border between East and West Sussex the first gunfire was reported and Emma Rugg took young Tom and disappeared, her house empty and door ajar one day with no word at all, though the rumours finally reached us that she had met a man in Brighton and jumped ship. Reverend Pickering suggested that when it came to Margery, a good shake was in order, but no one quite dared try it. The Reverend himself had been taking an alternate route through the village that meant he didn't have to pass Margery's room for some weeks now.

When the first strangers arrived they came not, as we had thought they might, by sleek-nosed cars reeking of 20th century villainy or chugging motorbikes that could be swerved and straddled and jockeyed to freedom, nor even by the rumbling murmurs of tanks we'd heard from Hastings, whose wheels had cracked all the cobblestones of the Old Town, but on horseback. We supposed it was, after the petrol shortages, one of the easiest ways to navigate the country.

The 25th of March, Feast of the Annunciation, hail, full of grace. Without meaning to, we walked quite quickly to Margery's room. We were anticipating some crack in the winter, or that she would be awake and expecting us. I suppose we were looking for a sign. Her windows were flung open, as though she was waiting after all, but we knew now that Margery did not care enough for us to come back, and that if there was hope or safety yet to be found Margery would not be its deliverer. The new spring leaves had come loose from their branches, drifting over her hair, and her face was buried against the pillows.

JANE FLETT

# Exactly The Thing That You Are

Before I joined the league—before the accident, my rehabilitation, *everything*—if I ever told a man what I was into, he'd look at me like I was dogshit. A turd wrapped in newspaper, propped on a podium, making a scientific pronouncement I was nowhere near smart enough to have researched.

'Don't you know it's fake?' he'd say. 'Don't you know it isn't a real sport?' To which I'd stick my tongue in one cheek and look up at him with my biggest, baddest, ohmygodREALLY? eyes. He'd say 'yes really Bella, it's actually all scripted' and I'd be like, well, glad we got that sorted out.

These days, if anyone tried saying a thing like that, I'd flip into a handstand, wrap my ankles around his neck, and slam him to the floor. He could explain to me whatever he wanted then, and I'd barely hear it with his lips slack against the carpet, the sweet muffle of drool.

'Not a real sport'—that's crap, by the way. It makes it sound like just about anybody could do it. As if all you need to do is put on a cute leatherette onesie, show up, and they'll tell you where to shove it. Well sure, they can *tell* you. Getting the script is easy. *Doing it* is the real sport. It takes more than words to fling someone over your head with a Pile Driver—it takes a pact with gravity. If I wrote those two words on a piece of paper in my finest penmanship and handed it to you in a sealed yellow envelope and said 'here's the script, babe!'…would *you* be able to execute the moves?

I'm not bitter. I don't expect everyone to understand. There are things I don't get too: long division and sudoku, mainly; food that's made to taste of flowers. But you know, sometimes when you don't understand, the best thing to do is shut your fucking mouth. You might learn something that way—like wrestling's a magnificent circus where the acrobats fall every time, and every time get back on their feet. Until they don't. You might end up with a fat mouth of roses—or tulips, there's something about the petals of tulips that always makes me think of thick animal tongues.

Anyway, this match. It's a chance to prove myself. Show the world I'm one of the good guys. Whatever happened in the past, things are going to be different this time around. It's an update from the House of Bella, a chance to catch up with the truth.

75

Today, I'm sat on the sofa at Hilda's, waiting for her to emerge from the sewing room. I am rabid with anticipation. Of course, the fight is what really matters, but the outfit is pretty important too. A girl needs to look good for her grudge match.

'Grudge match'—that's what they're calling it, in the newsletter anyway. The committee included a bunch of quotes about the accident from those who were watching, but the Wolverine just said, 'Well, we'll see what happens this time.' The Wolverine is six foot three inches tall and very secure in his own masculinity. He would never take being beaten by a girl to heart, or let it upset him so much that he couldn't meet my eyes in public again. The point is, if there's anyone holding a grudge, it certainly isn't either of us.

'You hold tight in there,' calls Hilda from the other room. 'I need to finish this hem.'

Even though I'm not together with Darren any more, his mother is my biggest fan. When I had my first ever bout six years ago, Hilda was the one in the front row, exploding in seal claps whenever I did a particularly dramatic flip, her tiny frame dwarfed by all those full-sized wrestling fans. My own mother tells me wrestling is unladylike. She doesn't like that I'm called Bitch Opossum. Apparently, it might give men the wrong idea.

When I came out to the stalls after that first match, globbed with sweat and facepaint, scabs congealing on my knees, Hilda didn't flinch. She wrapped her arms around me.

'Possum,' she told me, 'you are a real star. Brighter even than Dolly Parton.'

The excitement thrummed off her; her bird body shook like something plucked in my embrace. Then she pushed me to arm's length and told me all the moves I should have done differently to win. If I'd just held my breath for three more seconds. If I'd feinted left, he would have fallen right.

'Next time,' she insisted, 'I help you, and you win.' We'd eat oats together for a week beforehand, plain oats, the food of triumphant horses. Then, once my gut was clean as spit, she had the recipe for a coffee enema that would set me galloping home.

I tried to explain it didn't work like that, but she took my mouth and stoppered it up with cork ends and promises. 'I will make the outfit,' she promised. 'You will wear it and you will win.'

Hilda sews the most spectacular appliqué jumpers: barn owls with sequinned eyes, buggly dolphins, three-dimensional palm trees lapped by turquoise waves. I imagined myself in the spotlight, covered in glittered beasts, my arms spread wide. A tickertape of triumph catching and melting in my hair.

'Okay,' I agreed, and the coffee colonic was forgotten.

These days, when she's had a couple gins too many, her eyes will get loose and wet, and she'll tell me how much she wishes we were family. Not that Darren and I were still together. But that there'd never been a Darren—that she was my real mother, my birth mother, that the blood beating through my heart had come from her veins.

'All I ever wanted was a daughter,' she'll say, breathing hot juniper in my ear. 'Or, failing that, a Pomeranian. Something pretty that knows how to yap back.'

Not Darren. Not a boy, not even one who can cook hollandaise from scratch and who once came in third in the national Scrabble tournament, scoring 365 points on the word *Quixotry*. A real girl. A girl like me.

I've spent so many glorious matches in her creations, but it's been a while. Three years. And now, finally, I'm back where I belong.

'Ready,' she trills, emerging with a gleaming swatch of purple cradled in her hands like roadkill. 'Take it, take it, go on!'

I change in front of Hilda while she tuts and fusses at me, smoothing out the hemline and tugging at the gusset. When she is finally satisfied, I turn and look at myself in the mirror. I can't stop the grin. It's a skintight one-piece, cut low on the right shoulder, showing off the swell of my muscle. As I twist under the living room lights, the fabric flickers amethyst and electric. The neckline is studded with tiny white stones.

'Those are your teeth,' Hilda says. A snarly mouth, to go with the opossum face staring out from my tits, the fierce little eyes slap-bang on my nipples. 'I know, I know,' she says. 'They shouldn't be so sharp, for your sake as well as his, but I couldn't resist!'

I run a fingertip across them. Each is filed to a perfect jagged point.

'You'll be fine, don't worry about it. Just don't lean over too far.'

This makes me grin. I don't know which throws I'll be doing yet, of course, but I have the feeling the script will call for something dramatic. I growl at myself in the mirror; I feint to the left. My opossum meets my eyes and in a moment, all of us are laughing.

Back when I first started wrestling—when I very first started, before I found the league or anything—I made up all my own moves. I didn't have an opponent, or a ring, so I'd do it on the king size bed in Aunt Gayle's house. I'd wait until she went to the butcher, and then I'd rush into her bedroom and spend thirty minutes in the Wild Zone: the place where all that mattered was the sweet thunk of my body against the mattress, the pleasure of victory rushing through my teeth.

When I found the sign for the league, it felt like kismet: a thing left there especially for me. After all, how many of the other patrons of the Kwick & Kleen were secretly planning to become federation champions? They were all too preoccupied with y-front stains to spend four nights a week with a notebook, Chyna's best moves, and a battle plan. No. Whoever put up the sign <<WRESTLERS WANTED for AMATURE LEAGUE, ALL WELCOME>> had me in mind, even if they didn't know it.

At the hall, I was the only girl-shape in an ocean of muscly men. They stood in the centre of the room—slapping their forearms, pacing, making guttural 'huh' noises from the glut of their throats—while I waited by the wall and concentrated on moving my centre of gravity. The men did not seem aware of their gravities. They moved like sacks of testosterone waiting to be spilled, men who'd seen Fight Club one too many times and expected this to be the same thing. It's not. When you wrestle, you're a master of total control. There's no room to lose yourself.

By the second practice, all but three of them had gone.

Still, it was a shock to me too when I first fought another person. Muscle's not like feathers, or if it is, it's the white shaft in the middle. Stiff and sinewy. When I crashed into a real human body, it didn't give. Pain bloomed instantly, half flower and half wolf. I came home blossomed with bruises: purple horseshoes, thick blue planes across my thighs. I didn't mind. The congealed blood was a gift, a note in my skin that all of this was real.

Those of us who were left learned the moves. And, at the same time, we fought with blood. In the ring, you get to be two things at once: the thing you're scripted to be, and the thing you want to be. Your job is getting these realities to come into focus, like the red eye and the green eye in 3D glasses. When you manage it, all of a sudden the world leaps into one—one real thing in three glorious dimensions—and you become exactly the thing that you are.

Our trainer Fabian told us we'd know when it was time to take our fights public. 'IF YOU ARE STILL QUESTIONING,' he said, 'IT MEANS YOU ARE NOT THERE YET. WHEN IT IS REAL, YOU WILL KNOW.'

But waiting and questioning got boring fast, so one night I had a vision. It came to me in the night, in a dream. In the dream we were all tigers, but my tiger was the most powerful, the one that went for the neck. When I woke, I knew this was it. I was ready. I was *there*.

Fabian got very, very excited about my story. So excited, I almost felt bad—he'd been waiting for this moment a long time. The Great Fabretto was a killer once himself, but had to stop competing after the tracheostomy. There are seventeen different holds that will knock a throat tube right out of place. These days, he maintains his legacy by recounting endless stories of his grandest grand slams. He makes all of us listen. Sometimes, he cries.

Still, I kept up with the story. I described the orange of my tiger's fur, the wild snarl in the line of its jaw.

Fabian looked at me with tears in his soft brown eyes. He dug his fingers into the tops of my arms, and whispered to me in his robotic baritone: 'IT IS A SIGN. YOU ARE READY, ISOBEL.'

I was a hero. The triumphant leader of an eternal quest. The beast with the crown of vines, padding home to the villagers who'd sacrificed their sons.

I was a cheat. The tiger came from a documentary Fabian himself had recommended, about The Great Gama's rise from Indian village to the latex stage. I kept waiting for him to take me in his fists and ask who the hell I was trying to kid, but instead Fabian just slapped me on the back with two hands at once and told me I'd get my teeth for both of us. So I played dumb; I nodded eager. His excitement was a lifejacket that kept us both afloat. Because it was happening, it was really happening.

I was going to take it to the stage.

My first year as a wrestler was all travelling—showing up at a million hick towns to enact a story where the other team always triumphed. We worked with what the scriptwriters gave us. That's the deal; you get the story you get, and it's your job to play it. But as we got better—as the crowds got bigger—we started scheduling shows in our own town. There, we could be the ones who wrote the script.

If we wanted, we'd be the ones to win.

I don't mean to brag, but I got good. Real good. Not just at the fighting, but in terms of *ideas*. In the committee, I'd come up with the plays everyone wanted for their own match.

In my games, destiny twisted and writhed like a lizard's tail severed from its body. Just when you thought you knew where the plot was going, the script flipped to what you never would have imagined. The moment it did, it made sense. It was the only way it could have been.

In my games, there was no such thing as a heel or a babyface, not something innate. We were all human, we contained multiverses, and our narratives were as complex as our souls.

79

In my games, the girl sometimes won.

And it was perfect, it was all just-fucking-so in alignment—I'm talking spirit levels here, bubbles hovered between lines, I'm talking my actual spirit hung between the parallels of destiny—and then he had to ruin everything. Right in the midst of yet another debate about the headed stationery, Gregory the Grab raised one meaty fist in the air and declared his Radical Proposal.

Mayhaps, he said, it's not kosher for us to write our own scripts. Mayhaps we ought to appoint a board to make the decisions for us. Then we could concentrate on getting our bods that much stronger, and we wouldn't need to spend so much time *talking*. More time for the afterparty, know-what-I-mean?

It was stupid, of course it was stupid! A board might dredge up some semblance of a story, but we were the ones with kayfabe in our veins. Who at a board would come up with a twist like the time Masker the Unmerciful returned for revenge, just when we were all convinced Greg had won? Everyone loved that! The way he used the front benches? Hah! It even got a mention in the sports column of the local paper. So the others could quit, but me? I'd keep writing.

Apparently not, though. Apparently, that wasn't fair.

I was outvoted: eight to one. None of the others cared for coming up with stories. They were happy to slap on a nice tight outfit, to crawl onstage, to shut up and dance to a committee's choreography.

Idiots, every last one.

I don't like to watch footage of the accident, but some nights it's an ingrowing hair I can't help but gouge at. They still play it on the late night channel, on shows with names like *100 Sickest Real Injuries*, the ones where the presenters hold their vowels for three seconds or more. The voiceover always has to point out how shocked The Wolverine was—*he has NO idea what's coming his way!* They gasp all too hard when his leg snaps in two, they holler and howl over that white nub of bone. I hear it in the commentary, the twist of judgement. I didn't do what I was told. Of course, they don't say it like that. We're all pretending there is no *told*, that the girls lose because the girls are losers. Never mind how the board wrote them that way.

The first time it came on TV, I got so angry I nearly smashed the screen with my federation stamped ashtray (FOR WRESTLER ADVERTISING, CALL HULK SLOGAN). Even though I flipped the script, they all still bayed for him, contorting their lips at me in endless boos. They were scared, that's the thing—terrified of what could happen the moment we all stopped playing by the world's rules. The ashtray was solid and cold in my hand.

It was Hilda who stopped me. She took my arm between her hands and started massaging it with sharp little fingers. I was so surprised to be touched, I dropped the ashtray. By the time I'd thought about picking it up again, Hilda had changed the channel. The moment was gone. We sat there for a while, together, watching salmon leap upstream. In great flocks, just launching into the sky, straight in the mouths of the waiting bears. It's stupid really. You'd think they'd learn to find a better route. But it's programmed deep inside them, this need to come home regardless.

Fabian tells me the comeback special's my last chance. I say 'second chance' instead—it sounds better. 'Don't worry,' I say. 'I've talked to the tiger. It's going to be fine.' I laugh, waiting for him to join me. 'It was my period. You know how us ladies get!'

I slap him on the arm.

The reason they're letting me back at all is because I did Wrestler Community Service for three years. I stewarded the audience, wiped the pus and drool from the mat; I co-ordinated a publicity campaign that changed the entire fortune of the Hemingsdale Federation. No one gives two fucks about a football game any more, when fight night can bring the whole town together. It's a far cry from where we started, the squeak of the gym floor, the draft from the broken fire door.

The other reason is that these days, I'm pretty damn adored by the fans. Time softens all things, and today everyone wants to see the girl who put The Wolverine out of service for six months. On Wednesdays, Hilda helps me sort through the mail. We respond to *everyone*. The ones who write in crayon, the ones who include pictures of their dicks. Even the ones who threaten to teach me a lesson I'll never forget. 'Bless their hearts,' says Hilda. They all get the same thing: that headshot with my face all up in the camera, snarling, signed, and captioned.

'Break all the rules,' I write. And, 'Fuck the man. Fuck all men! xoxo'

It's finally happening this afternoon: the grand unveiling of the script. Hilda and I already went through all the things it might include last night, curled on her sofa, sewing some final adjustments to my bodice.

'What I really want's a good finisher, you know? Something that shows how much I've grown.'

'Oh, you'll get it.' She took the needle between her teeth for a second, folded over the line of fabric. 'It's what it's going to be, that's the thing.' The words muffled by metal in her mouth.

81

'The Cobra Clutch?' I suggested. 'It's a favourite. And it'll show my arm's strong again.'

'Ah yes, that's the one.' As she nodded, the needle glinted. 'No doubt about it: that's the one that will bring him down.'

'Well, we don't know that for sure.' I allowed myself a small smile. 'You know, maybe I'm not even going to win.'

We paused for a second, looked at each other, and burst out laughing. The needle fell to the floor.

Of course I'm going to win. What kind of story would it be if I didn't?

I'm here alone today, though. Hilda and Fabian are best kept apart. She calls him *that boy*, even though he's almost the same age she is. As in, *that boy doesn't appreciate you*, or, *that boy's an idiot, anyone can see*. It's the same as she said about Darren, and sometimes I'm inclined to believe her. There are moments when Fabian doesn't quite get it. In my darkest moments, I even wonder if he's on their side. But that's just paranoia. Fabian lives for me, for my training. When he looks at me, he sees himself, except younger and cuter of course.

'SIT,' he says, pulling a seat half out for me. I slide into it and lay my palms flat on the tabletop. No surprise attacks. 'HERE IT IS.'

I pause, just for a moment, letting anticipation unfurl inside me like timelapse footage of roses. And then I open the script and beam down at the first page. For a moment, I can't even read the words past the twitching of my heart. They switch and swirl, all tugging on my shirt sleeves at once. I force myself to pause. Touch my fist to my lips, take a breath, and go back to the first line. This time, I read it all the way through.

I swallow, and I read again.

'Fabian, what the fuck is this?'

'LISTEN...' he says, and then he doesn't say anything for a very long time. We just sit there, listening to the breath juddering in and out of his throat.

'YOU DO THIS.' he says. 'PLAY BY THEIR RULES. NEXT TIME, YOU WIN.'

'Fabian!' My voice rings pathetic in my ears, a high plastic whine. 'This was the whole point. Redemption. I want to be the good guy. I *need* it.'

Fabian shakes his head. 'NEXT TIME,' he repeats. 'THIS TIME, YOU EARN IT.'

I swallow the ball of phlegm that's creeping up my throat. Sat inside myself, I can feel my skeleton stretching all the way to my fingertips. This is what's left when the rest has gone. A heel, now and then and forever more.

All the way back to Hilda's, I think of different ways to word it. I want her to know it's not our fault. Next time, it'll be different. I want her to believe.

And then the door is open and she's right there in front of me. 'So?' Today, she's wearing the jumper with the pineapples done in green and in gold. The lemur stares up at me with its one googly eye. 'Tell me all about it. Tell me, my little pickle?'

I can't bear it. Are there even lemurs in Hawaii?

'How are you going to destroy him?' She presses her fingers against her temples in the international signal for mind reading. 'It's something all new. It's the Cobra Clutch, isn't it? Oh...oh, don't tell me. No, tell me now!'

How can I break the news that she's wrong? That we're both wrong? Not only am I going to get beaten, but I'm going to get beaten by *him*. That the fight will end with his foot on my face.

I look her deep in the eyes and force a smile to clamber across my cheeks.

'Let me surprise you,' I tell her. 'It'll be more exciting that way.'


I'm in the ring. I'm here, with the Wolverine. The world's all around me and I'm in its centre. The audience is chanting. Fat whoops and airhorns, and I can smell the collective held breath of anticipation, a thick animal fantasy to see a bone go snap once more. Oh, for the glorious white crest of a nub through muscle. The sputter. Droplets of crimson against the navy of the mat.

The rounds pass in great arcs, and I do what I'm told. In the breaks, I catch Hilda's eye. She gives me the two thumbs up, the ones that say: we're going to teach them a lesson. I grin in return, and my cheeks don't quite crack.

Somehow, eventually, it's the final round. We hurtle at each other. His body cracks against mine, and I feel it all the way up my bones. I lick my lips, tasting my sweat and his. And then I'm on the ground.

Tears prick in my eyes. Even though I knew this was going to happen—I threw myself down with his momentum, I did it—it breaks my heart. They're cheering for the other guy. They're ready for me to fail. This is the story they came to see.

I hear Fabian's voice in my ears: *NEXT TIME. THIS TIME, YOU PLAY BY THEIR RULES. NEXT TIME, YOU WIN.*

I close my eyes. Blood pumps through my body as I listen to the slap of the ref's hand against the matt: one...two...

I can get through this. We roll me onto my front and the muscles in my shoulders twitch as he digs my arms up behind my back. It's not that bad. It's not worse than most things.

If I concentrate hard enough, I can block out the chanting:

'Do—it, do—it, do—it,'
and
'Keep that bitch down!'

I won't cry in front of them. I twist my face into the mat and inhale sweat and old plastic; I kick my legs in the air, a toddler throwing a tantrum, like I was always meant to do.

And then I hear it. 'Stop that,' yells the voice, screeching louder than any of the others. Or maybe it's just that my ears are perfectly tuned to her frequency, a pitch only my heart and dogs can hear.

I prise my forehead up off the ground and look to the audience. Hilda's up and out of her seat. She's stamping towards the ring, hands in fists, and the crowds part for her like Moses. Why not? Who doesn't want to know what will happen next? A thin sweat pools against my neck.

Hilda clambers right up and over the ropes. When the referee takes a step toward her, she hisses. She bares the bright, white teeth of a seventy-year-old woman. Can he tell that they're false? I remember the first time I saw her without them, stood in the kitchen in the middle of the night, her cheeks loose and hollow.

The Wolverine grunts, and adjusts his foot on my face. A moment ago, my cheeks were on fire, but now the only thing I can feel is my own heart's holler. The Wolverine coughs—he's looking to the referee to call off the match. Grab her. Stop this madness. But nothing happens. The referee stands there, while Hilda strides across the ring and leaps on The Wolverine from behind.

'Let! Her! Go!'

The crowd are going wild. I've never heard anything like this, not even in the real championship games. Their voices rise up and around us, a wave waiting to break.

Right up until this point, I've been holding my own body down, letting The Wolverine pin me to the floor. But now I feel something rising up within me too. If history's written by the winners, why not be the one who wins?

For a moment, I let everything go. I stop pretending; I go slack. And in his flicker of shock, I crack my shoulders. I flail upwards, a salmon leaping from the water. A creature coming home at last.

Hilda's wrapped around his back, and she's screaming. Both of them fall to the ground.

I unfold my body, letting the pins and needles rush into my limbs. No one can quite believe what's happening. I clamber to my feet in the centre of the ring, I lift my arms above my head, turning slowly. I wave like the queen. In a moment, they'll stop me, but for now? I look at the Wolverine and crack my knuckles. For now, this—all of it—is mine.

JENNY KARLSSON

# I Shouldn't Be Calling This Late

## 1.

The tables and chairs are pushed against the walls and on the open floor lie dummies in a half-circle, black slits in lipless mouths, bold heads pointing to the centre.

After chest compressions the instructor says they can take five. There is coffee on hot plates and biscuits in a tin. Dusk is thickening over the field.

When Eva pours herself coffee, the instructor's reflection glides into hers on the window pane.

You do strong chest compressions.

Thanks.

Eva tries to hand him the coffee but can't shift the pot from her hand to his without one of them getting burnt. She puts the pot back on the hot plate. Drops hiss between metal and glass.

Maybe you've done this before?

Yeah I have.

I'm not surprised. Many people have. Then they're confident that they know what to do, until it comes down to it. When it's a sharp situation, they do nothing. People watch others die like it's the cinema. When my uncle died seven people stood watching.

Oh gosh.

That's why I do this job.

I'm sorry about your uncle.

Out on the staff car park wet snow is milling under the streetlamp.

You wouldn't stand by and watch though, the instructor says.

No?

No, I can tell from your chest compressions.

His eyes are a faded grey, pale as water, as if they once used to be blue.

After that energy refill – shall we?

Cups come down on tables and chairs. The employees return to the floor. An electric defibrillator is laid out next to each dummy.

The electricity must run diagonally through the heart, the instructor says and moves his hand across his chest like a saw.

85

Eva smoothes the electrodes onto her dummy as shown on the picture on the defibrillator – one above the right nipple, the other where the ribs curve under the heart.

What if it doesn't go like that? Dumb Paula saws her chest with her hand like the instructor did. What if you get it wrong and the electricity goes like this? Dumb Paula jerks her hand this way and that before her chest.

The instructor looks down at his dummy then straight at Paula.

There is no reason to get it wrong, he says.

Eva looks at Vaktis who sits at the other end of the half circle. He has his baseball cap in his hands and is wringing it like the neck of a small animal.

You don't need a reason to fuck it up though do you, says dumb Paula.

The instructor says, It's more important to do something than to do it perfectly.

Vaktis rises and comes at the doors too quickly for them to open. He takes a step back and adjusts the cap on his head. Then the doors slide open, cold air rushes in, and Vaktis walks out of the service house. Eva can see him on the car park. His back is in the light of the street lamp. The shiny fabric of his windbreaker catches the rain of light.

An exoskeleton of scaffolding cuts through the view from her kitchen. The windows in the next building shine white like rows of teeth in the dark. Silver clouds glide like oil around the moon. Eva has ironed a blouse for tomorrow and hung it on the door, name tag pinned to the chest. The phone is vibrating on the sill, her father's name on the screen. She thinks she won't answer it but then she does.

I was about to hang up.

I wasn't going to answer.

She hears her father take a drag off a cigarette. Smoke curdles his breath. The kitchen fan hums in the background.

I've sent you messages, her father says. I worry when you don't write back. I know you don't like me saying that.

The clouds float over the sky like they have somewhere else to be.

You're not at work, Eva says.

No, I'm at home.

Have you stopped doing night shifts?

No, once you've started–. But I'm going to speak to the pensions office.

She can picture the geraniums shedding dry leaves on the yellowed doilies on the sills, and she can hear the dog's claws clatter on the linoleum.

How is Kia?

She is calmer. She used to be edgy.

I know. Have you walked her?

We've been out.

The moon is a bright white hole. A blind eye.

Did you see the hills?

We didn't go that far. We went to the grave. The deer had eaten the heather.

She hears her father take a drag off his cigarette. She hears his breath get stuck then come loose.

Why did you call?

I just wanted to hear your voice. But I thought about it because it's Anton's birthday. I wanted you to give him my love.

I haven't spoken to Anton for a year.

But if you do, he says. You might. It's not too late is it.

Of course it is.


If one cooked, the other washed up. When they were poor they cycled around the parks at night collecting bottles and cans. In the evenings they curled up and watched horror movies.

Anton went to university to study graphic design. He was passionate about the difference between white and white. Eva's passion was less defined. Eva read magazines and Anton looked and her magazines and said the typefaces were badly kerned. He said it as if it were her fault.

Eva could tell she sank in Anton's eyes for not being critical enough of the look of the magazines. She could tell that Anton looked at her and thought she was common as muck. She could tell that sometimes Anton was frustrated and wanted her to be more confident.

I wish you were more–, he said, and when he couldn't find the last word he grabbed her shoulders and shook her.

When he let go, Eva asked, What is it you want in life?

Anton's eyes moved back and forth as if he were following something in the sky behind her – a bird or and aeroplane – but there was nothing there.

I want to be with you, Anton said. That's what I want.

He had looked scared then, and Eva had felt big, like she had a two metre wingspan.

I'm not in love with you anymore, she said.

It wasn't dignified when they split up. Eva didn't float or flutter but trashed her way out of the home she and Anton had shared. She did not consider Anton anymore. Her own incubating period was complete, proper experience about to begin.

87

She knew she had got lucky with the flat. A first hand lease is almost impossible to get. Such luck could only be a blessing – a nod from time itself. First she slept on a foam mattress on the parquet floor. Then the bed arrived, and she assembled it alone under a bare bulb.

In the beginning the city was her oyster. She made herself known in the bars, and the bars were happy to know Eva. She held her drink and paid her rounds then recuperated in her hundred-and-eighty bed, in her blessed flat.

The bed was the nicest thing she owned, stage set for the next act, for the middle. Eva longed ceaselessly for the middle. That's how she knew she was still only at the beginning.

## 2.

In the afternoon the snow turns to rain. Buses push slush up the kerb. A pigeon pecks on a Malteser in the sleet. Eva buys cigarettes in a news agent's on Nobelvägen because they help steady her nerves. A bell jingles against the door when she walks into Mafia bar. The instructor is sitting at the window counter.

I came early. I didn't want you to have to wait.

He looks feverish, glossy-eyed. He nods to the near empty glass by his arm. Would you like a beer?

A beer would be nice.

Eva unbuttons her coat and the instructor motions to the barman. She can tell the men know each other. She takes a seat.

The instructor is dressed differently than when he came to the camp site. Now he is wearing a short sleeved shirt and citrusy after shave, odd in the pit of winter. Be wary of anyone that feels like sunshine, her mother warned.

The instructor looks at Eva the way he might have looked at a fly that landed on his sleeve, and she regrets not leaving an empty seat between them.

Are you married? she says.

I have a girlfriend.

He takes out his phone from his breast pocket.

That's her.

He shows a photo of a woman with long charcoal hair and a little white bikini. Three little triangles over her three significant parts.

She's fifty-two but has the body of a seventeen-year-old.

He makes a noise that is half-laughter, half-snort.

I'm sorry, he says.

For having a girlfriend?

No for saying things like that. I shouldn't talk that way about one woman to another. It's not very respectful is it.

Eva leans to the side as the barman leans in between them.

It's up to you what you say.

The barman puts down two beers and takes away they instructor's empty glass.

I guess that's so.

Glasses clink.

We haven't been together that long, the instructor says. But we knew each other when we were young. We were lovers back then for a while. I was just beer and football, same as now, but Lilya was a clever girl. Went to art school.

His after shave makes her think of sand and water glittering like ground up glass. Lemony sunshine pouring endlessly. Up close the sun is a rat that licks the light from your bones.

But you didn't stay together.

The day of her graduation was the last day we were together. I watched her prepare for the ceremony. I sat on her bed as she put on the cap and gown. I was really proud, but at the same time it was sad.

Why?

All that formal stuff, it wasn't her at all. It was sad to see her submit to it, to see her be nervous and excited about the ceremony. It looked to me then like they had brainwashed her, so I told her when she goes up to receive her diploma she should say something, not just thank the dean, but say something different to make the moment specifically hers.

Out on the street a cyclist passes the motor traffic, sleet sprays behind the wheels.

And did she?

I don't know, I didn't go to the ceremony. Her parents didn't want us to be together, and she didn't stand up to them. Instead she went to grad school in Australia, far away as she could get. We wrote letters for a while, there was no Skype back then, but I think we both knew it was over. She would have known before me, being the clever one.

It was only a couple of years ago we met again at a gas station. She still makes art. She does light installations. Lilya Lazera she calls herself. It's a name her father made up. He was in the arts too. She was brought up proper middle class, cultured and smart but still funny. She was all that and with a darkness. As soon as I saw her at the diesel pump, I knew she still had her darkness. Sometimes it frightens me. I think if I would betray her she could take a knife to me.

89

So that's why we're here.

In some roundabout way yeah.

They sip their beers, looking out the window.

I hope she broke up with her dad, Eva says.

A teenage boy is pushing a pram through the sleet, shopping bags look about to fall off the handles.

Excuse me.

The toilet radiator is broken. The room is so cold she feels the warmth of her urine rise from the bowl. When she comes back there are two new beers on the counter.

Do you smoke?

Never. My dad died of lung cancer. It was my mum who killed him with her smoking.

Right.

Eva sits back down on the stool.

You don't have to put up with me. You can leave if you want. I'll understand.

I took two buses to get here.

The instructor gives another half-laughter, half-snort.

The instructor's name is Dino. Eva and Dino sip their beers while outside the window the traffic of Amiralsgatan contracts and dilutes to the rhythm of the traffic lights.

Lilya doesn't live here, Dino says. She lives out east where her kids go to school.

Oh?

She has ten thousand kids. She kept busy while we were apart.

Eva doesn't ask how many ten thousand are, nor does she regret coming.

As the bus pulls out from the central station her phone rings.

Sorry I talk so much, I got nervous.

Nobody gets nervous before me.

I think you're lovely, Dino says.

Outside the fogged up window, the city hangs like sheets of fabric. Street lamps pass at an even pace. Each light is a scratch on a dark surface.

You're lovely you're lovely you're lovely, he says like a prayer, like an incantation. Then a Skype signal goes off in the background and he says, I've got to go and hangs up just as the bus goes into the tunnel on Norra Vallgatan and all turns black.

## 3.

In the morning it rains. Mud seeps up through the grass and covers the field. Outside the reception, the driveway curves away like a black tongue under the candy stick barriers. The maple trees bristle wet. Eva sits at the check-in desk. Online bookings for the summer are trickling in. She allocates caravan pitches and sends confirmation emails with invoices attached. At lunch time the rain hardens to hail. The sky roars and ice beads lash against the glass front. Eva eats her lunch box and looks at the news. Another girl is missing. Then the downpour ceases and there is stillness again.

The back door squeals when she pushes it open. Out back Vaktis is squatting by a bicycle turned upside down. His fingers are black with oil. Bolts and washers are sprinkled on the ground.

Eva goes to stand under the awning. Water drips from its frayed fringe. There are seagulls on the roof edges and leftover rain in the air.

Vaktis rises and goes into the workshop. The bicycle's front wheel is spinning. The birds shuffle along the edge of the roof. When he reappears he has a broomstick in one hand and a tub of grease in the other. He comes and stands next to Eva, so close that their sleeves touch. She leans away from him.

Stand still.

He jabs the broomstick into the canvas. Rainwater slides down before them and crashes like a sheet of glass at their feet. Eva jumps back. Seagulls tumble into the sky like paper from a waste paper basket turned upside down.

You're an ass.

You didn't get wet did you?

Vaktis' grin shows three yellow teeth and the pink prawn-like flesh of his gums.

After her shift she takes the short cut over the field. The ground is spongy like a wet mattress. Rows of electric hook-ups poke up from the grass and mud, marking rows of empty pitches. Along the wire-net fence stands a handful of caravans with bits of stuff tucked away under tarps. This is February: occupancy below five percent and phones silent on the desk. Eva closes the gate in the fence and waits for the bus in the cone of light by the time table. Over *Monday-Friday* somebody has drawn a penis shaped like an empty balloon.

Dino lives in a block of flats around the corner from Mafia bar. The hallway is narrow and cluttered with shoes. The bedroom has purple wallpaper and a pair of jeans draped over the handle bars of an exercise bike. Light from a streetlamp falls through the blinds and makes stripes on the wardrobe. If she had friends, they would say she could do better than Dino who is twice her weight and age, has his team fading on his arm and a gut like the men she turns away from in pubs. He pushes himself against her bottom. The bed frame creaks, and the balance of the mattress unsettles.

It's not too late to go for a drink, he says.

Down on the street, a bus sighs to a stop at the kerb. A recorded voice calls out the name of the stop: Nobelvägen.

Maybe you could go down before me, he says. And I'll meet you at the bar.

She understands he needs to speak to the girlfriend in the evenings.

He kisses her neck softly – intimacy or a rehearsed imitation. Either way, it gives her a minor sort of rush. Her life now has a secret pocket. She now owns something scandalous.

She sits at the window counter on the same stool as last time. She unpins the name tag from her chest and lets her hands rest on the sticky wood. She takes in the sign shining above the bike shop across the street and the Jack Vegas machines in the corner and thinks that this might become their place, these their seats.

The beer fills her stomach one sip at a time. Briefly, she thinks of her mother picking slugs in the garden and the plastic bags full of black lumps that she forgot in the freezer.

The bell on the door jingles and a woman comes into the bar. The woman lays a clutch bag on the counter and takes in her reflection behind the bottles. Her posture is ballerina-like, something of youth preserved through to old age. Eva sits up straighter.

Dino comes jogging across Amiralsgatan. His jeans catch the red shine of break lights. He disappears out of view, then reappears on the other side of the glass. His profile is blurred by the rain.

He places a cool palm on her neck, a dry kiss on her temple. Like a dog Eva doesn't measure her wait by clock but is excited that he showed up to meet her. She pulls out a stool, thinking that now there will be something happening next, but Dino remains standing in a cold cloak of air.

She can sense it, he says.

His phone pings and the screen glows through his shirt pocket.

See? She has a sixth sense.

The phone keeps pinging with messages coming through like a string of pearls.

I told her I needed to buy toothpaste before the shop closes.

The barman comes over, and Dino's face lights up as the men shake hands. Through their smiles, the men say something to each other that Eva doesn't catch. Then the barman winks to her with one eye before he steps outside and lights a cigarette.

I would love for you to spend the night, Dino says.

The phone pings in his pocket. The slush-clogged noise of traffic comes in through the open door.

If you come over later I'll pay for a taxi. But I understand if you don't want to do that.

The barman paces up and down the pavement, wind tugging at the sleeves of his t-shirt.

I want to cook you breakfast, Dino says. It's just that–. He gives her a look that says it isn't his fault that he has a girlfriend, that he has that handicap to bear.

A girl out of humour makes flesh left for the flies.

Okay, Eva says.

Dino flinches.

Really?

I said okay didn't I.

You're great. Dino smiles. You're very easy going.

If he'd not doing it with you, he's doing it to you. Know you're spoiled with choice. Me, I don't recall picking my part. Her mother's voice sounded like a tire dragged through gravel. Her father dozed in the sun lounger. His leg was twitching as a horsefly clung to his ankle. The barman comes inside and serves Eva a new beer. It sits before her in a glass touched by so many other mouths, any number of lips nursing the same gold-coloured rim. The woman stands with her hands folded on her clutch bag like a pair of wings. Outside the window, the lights of the traffic stack up and dilute, stack up and dilute. Cars and buses moving in a jerky, uneven rhythm. This is the rhythm of a secret affair, she thinks, this rushing, waiting, rushing, waiting.

She eats yoghurt for supper and sits pushing the spoon around the edge of the bowl like the hand of a clock. The t-shirt drags in water from her hair. The blue light of a television goes out in the next building. The reflection of her face floats on the window like a thumb print on the glass. The sound of the traffic on the ring road comes through the ventilator split. When she first moved in she didn't understand what the sound was. She laid on the foam mattress imagining seas of air billowing with the world's turning toward the sun and a rivulet connecting her flat like an umbilical cord.

The inside of my womb was the only darkness you could handle, her mother said.

It's you and me now petal, her father said.

Eva picks up the phone and writes, It rains here all the time, then deletes it.

She writes and deletes:

I miss the snow

I miss

We had a CPR course at work

I wish

I'm s


One time she and Anton has a holiday with his family. They met in Gran Canaria for his brother's birthday. The dream is like that holiday, but different.

The family is gathered around a table at a restaurant by the water. The oldest brother raises his glass and says, This is what matters. The mother brings a tissue to her eyes. Fireworks crackle over the sky.

As the waiter comes to take the orders, Eva pulls back and slides discretely off the seat. Underneath the tablecloth it's cooler, but the floor is dirty. A rat runs across the tiles with a pickled cherry in its mouth. There are the mother's wedges and Anton's espadrilles. Then there is a pair of yellow plimsols. Beetles and broken glass stick to her skin as Eva gets on her hands and knees and crawls toward the yellow plimsols.

Then she is sitting up in the chair again. She and Anton are alone now. Two pizza slices are put down before them. Anton watches as Eva eats with her hands. He looks more and more bemused until held back laughter is making his eyes tear up.

What? Eva says with her mouth full.

As if by the flick of a switch, Anton's eyes turn cold. He shakes his head.

Tell me what it is, she says.

Are you not already full? Anton says. You spent all evening under the table.

Eva puts down the pizza.

Who did you like having in your mouth?

He leans forward to close she can feel the prawns on his breath when he says, Tell me, whose cock was the nicest?

She wipes grease off her mouth with a napkin. She has been caught. Anton is looking at her with dark triumph, with eyes like solar eclipses.

The restaurant floor is strewn with rubbish. There are chunks of bread, used napkins, and cutlery spread over the green tiles. A waiter strides through the dining hall carrying a silver dome. The tip of his shoe hits a desert spoon, sends it off tinkling against the tiles. Fireworks run like paint down the sky. Light pools on the black sea.

On the table is a bowl of pink ice cream with sparklers that crackle like rain on a tin roof. Anton is standing up and looking out of the window with his back turned to Eva. His shoulders heave like he is sobbing. It is hotter in the dream than it was in reality. Sweat runs behind her ears. A siren bellows out on the street.

She wakes up from her phone ringing on the bedside table.

It's raining heavily, drops as big as slugs clatter against the window.

It's late, Dino says. Did I wake you up?

Eva shakes her head.

No.

We ran out of time tonight. I'm sorry.

The shapes in the room are softened by the night, as if moss had grown on the furniture while she slept.

I can hear you're tired. I'll let you get back to sleep. I just wanted to show you something first, he says. See, I want you to understand, and I would try to just explain, I really would, if only I thought that I was able to, but I'm not good with words, so.

His voice sounds off balance. Booze-fuelled.

Okay, is all she can think to say.

The night is not fully dark. City light hovers in the flat like dust in the air. A blade of light glints on the television.

Are you there? she says.

Forgive me, he says.

She can hear him breathing on the other end.

I shouldn't be calling you this late. I should let you sleep. You should hang up and go back to sleep.

But you did call, so you wanted to.

Eva sits up with her back against the bed's steel curls.

What do you want me to understand? What do you want to explain to me?

Outside the window, some loose bit of scaffolding is clinking in the wind, something metal against something else metal. She hears Dino breathing on the other end of the line.

I'll phone back, he says.

When?

He has hung up.

The rain has stopped. The window pane is cool against her forehead, her skin oily against the glass. Down on the ground a cyclist is moving along the path. The bike light travels from one street lamp to the next, connecting the dots without connecting the dots.

The phone vibrates once. He has sent a message with only a picture. The photo is taken of the screen of his laptop during a Skype call.

Dark locks spill over tanned shoulders, the ends teasing blurry copper coin nipples. The torso is arching, as if drawn upwards by a string from the navel. Brought into focus are the spots and stubble where the skin has been shaved around the fleshy slippery parts. All significant parts of the girlfriend are offered without the white bikini–Lilya Lazera freed from the fetters of fabric.

Eva is still looking at the picture when Dino's number comes up on the phone. She answers without speaking.

Hello? he says. I'm sorry.

What for? You already told me she has the body of a seventeen-year-old.

He is quiet.

I'm not seventeen nor do I look it, she says.

I'm not good at talking. I'm just beer and football. I don't have a way with words, but I think what I mean is that I love Lilya, and I'm attracted to her, but she lives a long way away, and I'm also attracted to you. I feel very drawn to you Eva. I feel like there is something between us, something wanting to happen. When we were in bed, it was like we were inside a bubble and all of my problems were gone. Erased.

You said you thought she could stab you if you wrong her, Eva says. Maybe that's what you're after? Maybe you're looking to get punished for something. Maybe you're looking for repentance.

Do you want to come over? he says.

Not right now.

There is the parquet pressing up against the soles of her feet, the loose bit of scaffolding clinking outside the window, and the airy whistle in the ventilator split.

Is it light where you are?

Not yet.

Eva sees her skin reflect on the glass and thinks of the woman walking into Mafia bar where her youth floats in the mirror behind the bottles like a picture at the bottom of a lake.

You said your uncle died while seven people just watched. Is that true?

Yes.

Are you looking for me to watch you, and be ready to act?

You ask some funny questions.

There is her breath sticking to the window and his breath thick on the phone.

I can see some light now, he says.

He breathes in as if to say something more, but then he doesn't.

There is a scratch of light above the ring road, like a single fish scale in the sky.

Please don't be silent, she says.

What should I say?

Anything at all, as long as it is something that is specifically to me.

You're over there and I'm over here. You're looking at that light and I'm looking at that light. That's all I can say. I'm sorry. I don't have a way with words.

Please don't stop.

My name is Dino, I teach CPR for a living and I want us to have an affair. I don't know how it will go, and I'm not poetic, but if you'd like I can say *I love you* and then if you want to you can say *I love you too*. We don't have to mean it, but we could say it to see what it feels like.

As the sky brightens, her reflection fades from the window pane. The spaces between the cars going up and down the ring road shrink. Wet steel gleams and blazes in the white of dawn.

# Salva Nos

The couple came over the false horizon at a saunter. He had his arm over her shoulder and his jumper hanging loosely around his neck. She had a worn anorak tied at the waist and trailing in the dust and she held his fingers in hers so that her bare arm crossed herself at forty-five degrees and seemed to encourage his hand into her breast. They seemed utterly disinterested in everything around them; as if they existed independently of the downs and the cart track and the hedges and the fields. They didn't belong, they didn't.

Fragile was scraping dust off a pot shard. There had been some bits in the trench but nothing earth shattering. The oddest thing we had found was a limestone block with a neat Latinate letter S carved into it. On its own it meant nothing. He was sprawled on his belly like a kid on Christmas morning trying to get his head round a Meccano set; his eyes in the dust. Fragile seems to melt into the dust when he's on to something, like he belongs there. Fragile's never happy unless he's up to his knackers in filth of one sort or another. Right then he was wallowing around in a midden. Quite literally, and it wouldn't have mattered if the midden was as fresh as a Sainsbury's salad. If he thinks there's something in there, in he goes. Point of fact, I've seen fragile... actually that's not a good memory. Fragile was in the pit – trench #2 to be precise trying to tease another fragment of rubbish out of the dust and, as usual, oblivious. Norman, almost as accident prone as Fragile, had shoved a trowel through his hand that morning and was still at the A&E with Laura. Anyway the Land Rover was gone and someone else had gone on the chippy run. If memory serves there was only me, Fragile and one of the undergrads called Kevin. The dipshit.

Fragile didn't notice the couple. He wouldn't, because he wasn't in couple noticing mode. Fragile only sees what he feels he is supposed to see at a given time. So if we're on the pull, he'll notice girls and if it's dinner time he'll notice food. When he's in the pit, there's only "sign". In Fragile's register, everything in the pit is "sign". Sign of life, sign of death. Even the absence of a thing can be a sign. Once, Fragile guessed, quite correctly as it turned out, that we were working on a former mill pond just because there were no tree roots at a certain depth. We knew the river course had changed and that there might be old levels in the area but it was an inspired guess all the same. Fragile just has a nose for it. It comes of spending your summers wallowing in old middens and stuff. I'm partial to a bit of wallowing myself but I tend to look up a bit more. Two or three hours of wallowing at a time normally does me before I need a bit of sky. So anyway, I noticed the couple while Fragile was busy in the pit. Kevin, the dipshit, was sitting on the edge of the grave having a fag – probably a small joint actually since Norman was away.

They had stopped by the pit and were peering in. Kevin was kicking his feet idly, doing no favours to the walls and smirking up at the girl. I say girl, though she must have been twenty-something. It isn't easy to tell through sun burn and these two were very tanned. They were pretty bogging too. They looked like they had been hiking a long way but didn't have any gear with them. They both wore heavy looking boots and tatty jeans. He had sort of Australian looking hair: like he'd spent hours making it look that neglected and an aggressive outbreak of whiskers. She was one of those girls that would look stylish in a bin liner and quite possibly has at some point. I don't ogle people but with Norman at the hospital and Fragile in the pit I was sort of de facto site manager and I was a bit nervous of strangers trashing around: especially if they were talking to the dipshit. Anyway, I only ogled her arse for a second, saw they weren't going to be any trouble and rejoined Fragile in the pit.

Fragile's face was so close to the dust that perspiration had formed drops on his eyebrows that didn't have to fall to find the earth. The sweat gathered the dust and brought it up to his face. Small rivers had been carved down his brow from one side to the other. His left cheek was practically on the ground and his tongue protruded slightly as he fixed his entire attention on the clay coloured shard in the earth in front of him. He couldn't have looked more ridiculous if he had tried.

"Are you taking all day on that?" I asked. No answer. "It's only a fucking jug", I said.

"S'not a jug", he muttered, flicking the paintbrush over the cracked surface and scattering particles of dirt. The shard had acquired a dome shape as the brush gradually deepened the trough around it. "Skin us up half a doobie," said Fragile, not moving his eyes.

I got the fixings and checked the dipshit was still busy. The girl still had her back to us but the guy was looking around as if Kevin had exhausted his interesting conversation. That can take a while sometimes. Give him a gullible enough audience and he can do a passable impression of someone who knows what he's talking about. Just then they all looked just about interested enough in each other so I knocked up a single skinner, took a quick puff and handed the tubette down to Fragile. Fragile managed to disengage his left hand just enough to take the spliff and moved his face away from the shard as he inhaled, but his eyes stayed on the shard.

It was while I was sitting on the edge of the pit like that, sucking on the remains of a spliff, that I saw what Fragile was at. Possibly the gear worked on freeing up my imagination – Fragile's a great believer in the power of THC to help you see through the fog – but more likely it was the shifting of the sun, moving shadows in such a way that what had been obscure became clear. Anyway, just as the guy turned up and I was surreptitiously crunching the dead roach underfoot I saw what Fragile was at.

"You wouldn't expect to find that, would you?" I looked up but the guy was just a silhouette with the sun behind him. I smiled. "Not in a midden", I said.

"Does it mean anything?"

I shrugged. "We dig up and document. It gets interpreted later."

"Is it a man or a woman?" he asked, a bit idly. His boots were of good quality but scuffed and worn. They had no laces.

"Difficult to..."

"Adult male", said Fragile without looking up. He had the brow ridge exposed by this time and most of the square brow was visible. For some reason I felt stupid for having missed the obvious. The guy was making me feel stupid.

"Can you date it?"

I started to speak but hesitated. Fragile still didn't take his eyes off the object. We had been clear about the date of the level but this cast doubts. Something about the guy made me feel insecure and exposed. "We don't interpret at this stage," I said, more defensively than I had intended.

The girl joined him and they wrapped their arms round each other. She was very dark and her black hair hung in a tatty curtain across her face. When she spoke her teeth looked unnaturally white. "Is it a man or a woman?" she said.

"Adult male," said the guy. Fragile glanced up briefly then went back to the dust.

"Look," I said. "Nobody minds you looking around but the boss will be back soon and he'll be in a mood because he took half a finger off this morning. If he gives you any shit, pretend you're students or something. He hates tourists"

"We aren't tourists," said the girl.

"Everyone's a tourist who isn't holding a trowel as far as Norman's concerned," said Fragile from the dust.

"Norman?"

"Professor Norman. He'll be all right with you if you tell him you're students. Might even make you a brew and show you round. Just say you're doing history or archaeology or some shit. Only don't say you're from Cambridge for fuck's sake."

They both smiled but in an indulgent sort of way. Then I had an after-thought. "You aren't students, are you?"

"Not in any formal sense," said the girl, a bit contrived. I thought – yeah, I bet.

Norman was in a foul temper when he got back. Laura looked like she needed a drink. She slammed the Land Rover door and stomped into the marquee. Norman stalked over to the caravan with his left hand, wrapped in gauze, waving in the air. He mellowed a bit when he was told we had a corpse in trench #2. He got someone to make him a sling out of a pillowcase and, after a good slug of Glenfiddich, he manoeuvred his carcass down into the pit for a good poke around.

"Isn't a burial," he said.

Fragile was sitting by the trench in a director's chair drinking a tin of ginger beer, covered in dust. He seemed a bit distracted, gazing off at the low hills. When you focus on something close up for hours on end your eyes need to rest. Down in the pit some ribs and vertebrae were exposed and the lower jaw, hanging wide of the cranium, was emerging from the earth.

"Teeth are quite worn," said Norman.

The couple were still around, hovering near the hedge on the other side of the marquee talking and occasionally giggling to each other.

We knew it wasn't a burial because it was too shallow and, by and large, organised burials aren't placed in rubbish tips on the edge of villages.

"Looks very healthy. Big chap," muttered Norman, more to himself than us. We had noticed the heavy cheekbones and brow ridges. Norman picked a few lumps of earth away with his pen and sucked air in. "Aha, Just as I thought. Arthritic changes in the right scapula ball joint. We've got a labourer: blacksmith or similar."

"Which?" said Fragile, suddenly. Norman ignored him.

I couldn't work the hostility. Fragile despised Norman as much as anyone but he had snapped and now was glowering at the back of the boss's head.

In the pub later, Fragile looked distracted. I said, "Ignore Norman. He doesn't know a blacksmith couldn't be a labourer."

Fragile looked over my shoulder to indicate he wanted a change of subject. I followed his gaze and saw the couple in the corner. She was playing the fruit machine and he was watching her.

"Anyway", I said. "You have to admit..."

Fragile gave me an indulgent look, but I was thrown by the lack of interest. He had been annoyed enough to toss a barb at Norman earlier but clearly couldn't be bothered to discuss it now. "The corpse could as easily be an archer as an artisan", he said. "The point is, a blacksmith and a labourer are two different things".

"I know", I said. Fragile had gone somewhere else in his head though. He necked his pint and waggled his empty glass. I nodded and Fragile went to the bar.

The couple were still giggling by the fruit machine. She glanced over at me a couple of times. Kevin appeared beside them and I heard him explaining some stuff. He did that thing that he does: curling his hand all around the glass like a spin bowler grasps a corkie and holding it close to his chest while his upper body rocks backwards. I don't know why but it's a posture I associate with country people. Kevin would have a *Young Farmers do it in Tractors* sticker on his car if he ever passed his test. He looks agrarian does Kevin with his wooly jumpers and fashion free hair. Odd that: he comes from somewhere in Manchester originally. I imagined him explaining the dig all over again and volunteering his expertise in the interpretation of the bones. The girl looked indulgent but her bloke seemed genuinely interested. He asked questions and nodded and cocked his head occasionally like an undergrad in a tutorial. After a minute, he produced a packet of Lambert and Butlers and the two of them went outside.

And like a fox waiting for a dog to go to sleep, there was Fragile handing her a pint. She smiled at Fragile, sipped at the drink and said something. Fragile gulped his beer and said something back. He didn't seem to have another drink so I assumed the bitch was having my pint. Either that or he had never intended to get me one in the first place. I gave it a few seconds and went to the bar myself. I had to go right by them and they didn't even see me.

I got cracking to a couple of locals at the bar and later had a game of pool. I didn't see the girl again that night but at closing time I thought I saw the boy in the car park. He was by the woodshed in shadow and there were two or three other guys standing there smoking. When he puffed on his fag, his face lit up a bit but I couldn't be certain it was him. There was no sign of Kevin.

Next morning Laura kicked the tent as she passed. It was late and I felt bad. There was no sign of Fragile which didn't surprise me at first as he usually beat me to the works but it soon became clear that Fragile hadn't been in the tent. I dragged myself to the works where the undergrads were standing around waiting for someone to tell them what to do. There was no Fragile, no Kevin and no Norman.

Laura was cradling a coffee mug and scowling. The works hadn't been secured last night and a breeze had come up and tipped a bucket full of trowels into #2. The tarpaulin over the body had come loose on one side and was flapping in the dust.

"Norman's gonna freak," said Laura.

"Where is he?" I said and felt the stabbing pain in my throat for the first time.

"In bed," said Laura. "He's got a cold."

She tipped out her cup and climbed down into the trench. I rounded up some of the undergrads and got them to help her then went to the mess tent to find some Paracetamol. I took a pint of strong black and forced down some cornflakes but the queasiness wouldn't shift and the headache just seemed to get worse by the minute. By about nine o'clock I was finding it hard to swallow. About ten, Norman surfaced and he looked a bit like I felt.

Down at the pit, Laura was directing two of the undergrads when the boss came up. I was sifting soil with the volunteers and could hear him snapping, "There. No there. To the left. No, left for goodness sake... Oh for God's sake give it here." Even through the thickness of his constricted throat, I could sense the excitement and I left the dust to see what was going on. Laura and the youngsters had stepped back while the boss got down in the trench. She looked up when I came to the edge of the pit and said simply, "We've got another one."

It was hard to focus in the brightness between the scudding clouds and I had to go back into the marquee to work on the shards and metalwork in the relative dark. Even there the pain behind my eyes was too much and after lunch (which I skipped) I gave in and crawled back into the tent. There had still been no sign of Fragile or Kevin.

The fever dreams were vivid and surreal. I seem to remember my mother at one point shouting, "How do you get 'flu' in the middle of July?" There were great mounds of freshly dug earth and columns of people marching down towards long pits, like parallel scars on stark, flat fields. There was some sort of festival going on with people singing and dancing round in circles but their smiles seemed odd, sort of fixed, and they all had loose, dry hair that bounced at the wrong pace, taking a moment too long to fall back onto their shoulders as they twirled. There were bands playing; percussion and wind with no strings and the music was chaotic and almost formless. I followed a line of people down towards the trenches, past herds of thin looking cows, between empty cottages and overgrown gardens. One of the bands of musicians was resting on a dry stone wall. They all smiled their flat, fixed smiles and one of them played a scale on a flute which I saw was actually a long bone.

My skin was crawling and every joint was burning. I felt weak as a kitten and my head: Oh Jesus, my head. I climbed out of the doss bag and ripped the tee shirt off, used it to mop the surplus sweat out of my pits and tossed it on the ground outside the tent. The hot space in there stunk bad enough, I reckoned. I felt chilled without a cover though and rummaged through the crap until I found one of Fragile's jumpers and hauled it on. I shambled over to the marquee and necked a pint of water, swiped a pair of shades someone had left lying around and made it down to the pit.

Norman was sitting on the edge, his right arm filthy up to the naked elbow, his left hand still held at shoulder height with the black fingertips visible above the grimy bandage. He was grey and thin looking and his eyes seemed to have receded. But he was leaning forward, intent on the action in the pit. "Gently now," he was saying. "That's the way. Just test it. Let it give. No. OK you'll need to brush some more from under the clavicle." I looked down to see one of the undergrads, belly down in the earth for all the world like Fragile, teasing bones out of the dust with a paintbrush and a palette knife. Norman's instructions were being delivered in a measured, almost nurturing tone and I just couldn't work it. It just wasn't Norman.

Laura was sorting bits from the spoil and I made it over to her. "Don't breathe on me," she said.

"Have you seen Fragile?" I croaked.

"Dropped by earlier," she said. "With his mates."

"Eh?"

"Those two tourists."

"And the Dipshit?"

Laura shrugged. I looked down at the trays under the sieve. There was a wealth of stuff there; buttons and pins and buckles and a scattering of coins. A conical steel object was recognisable as the tip of a modern ploughshare. I said, "Anything interesting in the silver?"

"All fourteenth. Low denomination. Scrap."

Laura was in her usual state of dismissive cynicism, which belies her intense professionalism. I bent and picked up a cracked silver ha'penny. It was worn and bent and similar to hundreds of others I had handled:

104

working money that had been through the hands of dozens of small and medium people. The silver was certainly adulterated with lead which would make it wear quicker. I could just make out, *Edwardus Rex*.

"That looks like a lot of money to find in a grave," I said.

Laura had lit a cigarette and puffed a cloud of smoke in my face. "This isn't a grave," she said. "Seen these?" She pointed at a collection of square stones, building blocks by the look of them. Several had capital letters chiselled into them. I could make out an S, an L and possibly an N on separate blocks. The letters were neat and professionally cut. "Was our blacksmith a mason?" I asked. Laura shrugged.

I kept getting the image of the musician with the thigh bone neatly drilled with holes to make it into a flute. The lines of marching people with disconcerted hair. I didn't know then where the question came from but I blurted, "How many bodies in the pit?"

Laura sucked deep on her gasper and shrugged again. "Bits of at least four so far."

"Including the blacksmith?"

Laura smiled, as much as Laura ever smiles, "No, your blacksmith's in the can. We think he was later. Doesn't seem to be connected with the others." She shrugged again. "Just coincidence."

My brain was bleeding. I couldn't process the coincidence of a rough burial on top of an apparent mass grave that seemed to contain valuables. It seemed just too much coincidence. However my brain was really bleeding. "Laura," I said. "I really have to go and lie down." She shrugged and I retired to the tent.

I dreamed about Fragile and the tourists. They were dancing in a field of daisies that sloped down to a small stream. The tourists looked healthy and energetic but Fragile was thin and sick and seemed to struggle to keep pace with their movements. I looked down to the stream and noticed an older man with his back to the meadow. He was gazing across the stream and making small waving movements with his right hand. As if he was trying to attract the attention of someone on the other side but there was nobody there. The girl noticed me and said, "He's lost a pearl". I looked over and watched them dance for a while. Fragile had stopped and was just standing with his arms folded over his chest. His skin was grey and loose and his clothes were muddy and torn. The couple kept dancing, lifting their feet high in the air and almost floating over the grass and flowers.

Later, I was aware of someone in the tent and I smelled coffee. The light had changed. Later still it was dark. Sweat trickled down my sides and pooled in the sodden fabric of the sleeping bag. My throat burned and my head throbbed.

There was no sun yet and the early daylight was filtered through low clouds. It was cooler and the air felt heavy and pregnant with rain. I shambled over to the pit in a pair of shorts, enjoying the cool air on my hot skin. I thought I saw someone in the dimness beyond the hedgerow at the edge of the field and assumed it was a local walking a dog. The dig was quiet. I tugged the tent peg out of the tarpaulin loop and heaved the sheet off to one side.

A lot of work had happened in the pit. They had gone down nearly a foot and uncovered what looked like a road made of even blocks of limestone. Similar to the blocks with the letters that Laura had cleaned up. I noticed the road had quite a severe camber. In the middle of the pit the road seemed to have been dismantled leaving a hole about eight feet long and four or five wide. Near one end of our pit a wall foundation crossed the road. The bones of a number of skeletons were heaped in the gap in the road. It all seemed wrong. Why would they dig up a paved road to bury people? Then I saw it.

It was the wall that gave it away. When I looked closer I saw that the foundation didn't cross the road at all. The road was built up against the wall. The building, whatever it was, had not post-dated the road but had already been there when the road was laid. It was obvious really. And of course it explained the camber. I was actually looking at the roof of a cellar. They had broken into a cellar from above to inter the bodies. Which suggested that the heap of corpses was as deep as the cellar: however deep the cellar was. I was doing mental arithmetic, based on typical contemporary church crypts and wine cellars. It was at least eight feet to the wall, possibly as long again in the other direction. It would have to be at least six or seven feet deep, possibly more. I was thinking in cubic yards. The heap of bodies could be huge. I shivered and shambled back to the tent for some clothes.

Norman was in his element.

He waved the red dot from his laser pointer around the image on the screen. "The North wall of the Nave with the floor slabs still in place."

The students nodded dutifully and made notes at appropriate moments. Beside me, Laura yawned. "In this next picture, the floor plan is clearer. Floor slabs have been systematically removed, no doubt recycled when the site was re-occupied in the sixteenth century. The rougher stone of the crypt roof was brought from the Marlborough area and we suspect

106

belongs to the later phase of the building, probably thirteen-nineties. The church itself is Norman". He smirked. "No, of course, I'm Norman; you already knew that." The students chuckled indulgently.

Laura was doodling on her pad, making intricate swirls with her biro that poured over the paper like waves on the sea. Norman changed the image again. "The Blacksmith. We call him that but we don't know he was a Smith. Definitely a labourer of some sort."

"Which?" I muttered. Laura looked at me sharply.

"An anomaly. Something of a mystery, this. He doesn't belong to the other burials but he is roughly contemporary. There are no signs of violence this is an organised burial not a murder or war victim. And he is actually beside the hole in the crypt roof and not in it. We suspect it could be pure coincidence that he's there at all and we have no idea why he's there. For a free drink in the refectory, who can spot the most unusual aspect."

There were murmurings but nobody spoke. "Come, come. It smacks you in the eye. Remember this is a Christian church. Albeit effectively deconsecrated at the time it was used as a plague pit."

There were a number of ah-has. "Right," said Norman. "We would normally associate crouched burials with pagan society. This is a burial but it's not a Christian burial."

He brought up the next picture. "The letter stones." The blocks with the neat letters were laid out in a line on a trestle table. S-L-V-N-S. "Prize for the most inventive guess but I'm afraid a guess is all we have. Somebody carved these letters on the inside of the crypt before the bodies went in or, less likely, on the stones that were removed to make the hole in the roof. Yet another mystery, I'm afraid, and probably not associated with the burials at all."

Back in the post-graduate centre, Laura and I sipped a glass of cheap wine and went through the motions of preparing papers. Our hearts weren't in it. Laura fingered the postcard. "Norman's going to publish a monograph on this shit."

"Someone should," I said, trying to be generous. "It is unusual."

She turned the card over in her hand. I could see the medieval tithe barn on the front and Fragile's unmistakable handwriting on the back. The barn is less than five miles from the dig and the postmark told us that it was sent the day after he went missing. We haven't seen him since.

"What does that mean?" she said.

"It means, 'save us'," I said. Laura looked at me, slightly angry. I apologised. She tossed the card onto the desktop and it landed face down, Fragile's writing facing up at us. I read the words like a prayer. *Salva nos. Salva nos. In nomina Regina cellorum, salva nos.*

ALISSA JONES NELSON

# Al-Watan

Mohannad surfaces to newly familiar mansweat nipping his nostrils, Rahim shouting from the next bed. Rahim is a language he doesn't understand. A few flat, colorless words of nomadic English string them together in daylight. But in the middle of the night, when the nightmares submerge him, Rahim leans out of bed and spills a steady stream of invective in Benadiri until Mohannad sweats himself awake, the darkness of their shared room unbroken by the darkness of Rahim's skin.

Two sets of bunk beds crammed into ten square meters. Mohannad has one drawer in the communal dresser and half the space under the bed. The other half belongs to the Pashtun sleeping soundly above him.

Adrenaline alive in the dark, he wonders how water remembers a drowning.

Terror is a slick thing inside him, a wet mink, fanged. He chases it down, grabs for it with numb fingers, but it slithers through his hands before he can squeeze.

\*\*\*

How much do wet shoes weigh?

Look down.

He looks sees racehorse legs just two where his own should long slim bones knees bent the wrong how to keep afloat or kick toward the surface when the weight of moon-shaped iron shoes drags hooves-first toward the bottom trapped in this devastating body the saltwater churns with human limbs inky black on white froth shrieks like a hare the instant before a pack of wild dogs pure terror bleached blankness gorging seawater tastes like blood pounds sinking panic crests breaks ebbs his world fades quiet          the wrong color water presses in on memories of Mediterranean turquoise teal cobalt cornflower sapphire seafoam electric baby royal lapis overexposed postcards of the past a thousand and one miles a thousand and one reprints treed in white wire cages sunk in fiendish summer asphalt guarding icy hotel lobbies eternally dreaming that brilliant azure blue but nightmarish

108

sharp grey slate cold sea seizes the present merciless faithless bottomless unexpected

He knew. Of course he did. But every single person on that popped balloon of a raft had to believe it would be different.

\*\*\*

Rahim already has his visa, has managed to find work driving a white delivery van through the early morning streets. The bitter bite of instant coffee crystals cuts the frigid fog of 6am. Sometimes Mohannad rides along, helps carry the crates.

'Please, my friend. It's not a good idea.' Mohannad shifts nervously in the passenger seat, tries to smile through the glass at a woman staring past. Two umber men parked illegally on the margins of the Platz in a white van at rush hour. He lifts his eyes to the shaft of windows, exposed, a fish in a bowl. Just over his head, white lace curtains flicker. A wrinkled woman as wide as the window, chin at the sill, blue hair crimped into waves. He feels the hot breath of her stare. The curtain falls. He imagines her arthritic claws on the telephone. It's only a matter of minutes.

'I cannot stop for a cigarette?' Rahim with his known unknowns smile, his billy goatee. Asylum has transformed his skin color into a problem he can't solve. Spreads his rosy palms, cracks the window. The flare of the lighter strings an acrid tang through the air between them.

'You push too far.' Mohannad fastens his eyes to the white lace curtain. 'Every time? Why?'

'These people,' Rahim narrows his eyes at the commuters sluicing toward the subway. 'Their fear.' He exhales the word with his smoke. 'I can smell it like one of their Bratwurst.' He lurches out a laugh and swings his deep eyes to Mohannad.

Rat-a-tat-tat on the window. Mohannad's heart springs, lands on the back of his tongue. Polizei black and blue, one hand on the thick belt riding his hip. Rahim puts on his refugee. His recent German lilts and tumbles south. Unfailingly polite. A call? Really? Can't park here? Oh, sorry, so sorry! Yes yes. Right away. Already reaching for the ignition. Clutching the illusion of control.

The tiny explosion of his cigarette as it sails out the window. Nostrils flared over his stiff grin as he pulls away. The policeman grunts, taps the registration number into his screen.

Rahim needs his daily dose of that musky slinking stink of fear through the crack. Just another pheromone in the driver's seat.

Alissa Jones Nelson

\*\*\*

Friday afternoon, Rahim prays with the others. Mohannad hides in their room with the onionskin pages of a creaky leather Bible, red circles the words he doesn't understand. Shouting knifes the tension in the communal kitchen. An ocean of differences compressed into firework arguments over food, dishes, dirt, space.

The door bursts inward, the wall shudders. Rahim looms.

'Elias is cooking pork again.' Rahim's wide white teeth split his face. 'The food police are taking care of it.'

Rahim, who'll gladly eat Currywurst when nobody's looking. Since washing up in this city, he prays five times a day. Fasts during Ramadan. Lets his frayed temper unravel around the edges of the faith that stands in for home.

'That book looks like chicken pox.' Rahim's weight barely tilts the mattress as he settles. The shrieks in the kitchen crescendo, cut off.

'You rice Christians.' His mullah voice. 'Haram.'

Rahim's opinions are black and white with square corners.

'Elias isn't a convert.' Mohannad avoids the Iraqi Christians, their stories of churches bombed into abattoirs, the way they wear their pain so close to the surface. 'Why not let him eat what he wants?'

Rahim aims his fierce gaze at the flat white wall that does nothing to shut out the constant static of human life pressing in. 'Nobody here gets to eat what he wants.'

Mohannad fingers the delicate chain of the glittering cross around his neck. Rahim catches the gesture.

'Monday, isn't it? When the bureaucrats decide whether your God is God? Whether you stay or go back?'

Mohannad lets the anger rise up into his mouth, bump up against his teeth. Runs his tongue over the bitter tang of it. Swallows. 'Yes. Monday.'

When he first stepped off that train in Berlin and the November air reached in and yanked his lungs up against his collarbone; when the camp offered the lower half of a rickety bunkbed in a playpen of a room split with three strange men; when the women washed their children's clothes in the foot-pumped water of temporary plastic sinks and there'd been no water left to brush his teeth; then he found the church. Two meals a day, German lessons, the simple dignity of listening. And her. Three afternoons a week she volunteered. Helped him fill out the endless paperwork it takes to enter the refugee race. And now he's straining for the finish line.

He rises as Rahim lets the Bible slip through his long fingers to the dusty floor. 'I'd better get going.'

110

'You with your white woman on the weekends.' Rahim's skeletal smile stretches. 'One of the lucky ones.'

\*\*\*

Wide awake in the darkest part of the night, he elbows himself up to watch her sleep. Curled away from him like those backward quotation marks in her language lean away from the words instead of embracing them. He'd asked her the all-important question two weeks ago, under the long shadow of his asylum hearing. Chewed the insides of his cheeks raw while she hesitated with her yes. He needs her to translate the strange familiar. Needs that ring on her finger to anchor him to dry land. Isn't love always more or less fear and need dressed in other words, a suspicious package wrapped up tight in bright metaphor? After everything, falling in love feels like winning a war. He stretches trembling fingers toward her bare shoulder.

She feels him shift on the mattress behind her and opens her eyes without moving. Keeps her breathing slow and even so he won't. Sometimes she dreams the small mattress they share is a raft, endless mirrored sea rolling to every horizon. She dreams of plucking him from the ocean. When he's wet tawny gleaming from the showers he takes after sex, her wide golden hardwood buckles, and she sees him standing on a gravelly beach, caped in a crinkled silver emergency blanket, staggering under the weight. It's all there behind the smile he stretches tight for her on weekends.

The ring she bought for her own finger glows like phosphorescence in the jaundiced dark of the city night. When he'd asked, her suspicion had flattened her. Just a month now till her roommate moves out. Then he'll be here every night. If they let him stay.

She holds herself still, listening to him twist in the tangled sheets. Feels him heave out of bed, bob down the narrow hall to the bathroom. Squeezes her eyes shut against the light, the slow drip of water.

\*\*\*

Saturday trip to the sauna was her idea. To relax, she said.

He fingers the meager hamam towel cinched tight around his waist. Declines the Dampfbad because he'd have to strip. At the entrance, a sign in German and English: textile-free facility. Bathrobes required in the restaurant. Thirty years old, his first taste of champagne. The musky grapeskin tweak in his nose.

'We're getting married,' she explains to the waiter. Mohannad stares into the polished gleam of the ebony table, champagne bubbles in the reflection racing each other to the bottom.

111

'Relax,' she holds her glass out to him. 'It'll be fine.'

It's an I'm-not-staring contest. He does his best not to notice their pendulous breasts, their languid cocks in nests of varicolored hair. They pretend not to see him at all. Here, where everyone is naked and strange, he might be able to pass. If he could mimic their nonchalance. She schools him.

'They're just,' she struggles. 'Bodies.'

He barks a watery laugh.

'What's funny?'

Cultural immersion, naked in a pool of tepid jade water under their grey February sky. Sink or swim. He stretches his long strong legs straight out and floats, feels the lick of cold where his barren skin breaches the water. His own ragged breath fills the silence.

***

Sunday morning, thick grey stone walls deaden godless sound from the street and echo back the foreign cadence of the liturgy. Ancient words, also travelers from a distant land. The sweet scent of golden wax, the sharp candle smoke, the air-raid boom of the organ wash over him.

He doesn't understand all the words, but he's learned when to stand, when to kneel, the cold seeping into his body through his knees. He sits before a pale marble statue of Mary in her chador, only her mild face showing, a vase of Amaryllis at her feet. Her face reminds him of Nargis, the Iranian refugee whose legend circulates a warm current through the winter camp.

Nargis had shared her whole conversion story. Facebook, Twitter, Jesus, baptism. Until whether it was genuine wasn't the question anymore. What mattered was whether the Guardian Council would believe. What corrective steps they might take if she were sent back. Her asylum had been a foregone conclusion. So had the funeral her parents staged for her in Iran. Easier to explain a dead daughter than a Christian one.

His fiancée's bowed head swims in the corner of his eye.

After the service he stands next to her, angled into the narrow space between pews. A swelling congregation, on the ebb for decades until waves of converts broke over the altar. They all know. Tomorrow. The pastor wades up in walrus robes, offers his blessing. Discusses the details with her, the voice of authority. Mohannad the little lost lamb, wandered away from his flock. She gets to play the savior.

The other hopefuls come to wish him well. They scent his fear as he reads their envy. There are only so many places. They wring his hand.

112

Everyone eyes the flash of gold on her finger. Eyes wink, heads nod. He wonders how many of them know that the answer to the question about being your brother's keeper is Yes.

\*\*\*

He'd been a vet. Specialist, expert. A stable of sleek rare racehorses. Sweet straw and dancing dust in sunlight. Sloping Nefertiti profiles reaching across the wire. Some days his arms ached with their exuberance. But that was elsewhere, before. Time and distance are slowly converging into a single point on the horizon, home stolen daily by dimensions innumerable in months or miles. Some days his arms still ache.

Her parents were impressed. Relieved. Talked about qualifications, exams, job opportunities. A current of respect running under the surface. Even here, oh yes, on the margins of the capital.

'Not racehorses, but plenty of little girls with rich parents.'

'Get there on the train.'

'The language would be a problem.'

'But you must learn. After the wedding?'

That word wedding always dragging a question mark after it like a security blanket. They draw their own conclusions on the walls of their familiar. She'd held his hand the first time, promised not to let go and hadn't. This icy white afternoon, she sits in a straight-backed chair on the other side of the room. He's adrift on the sofa alone.

'When should we arrive tomorrow?'

'Half an hour before, I think.'

'Will it be enough?'

'What does one wear to an asylum hearing?'

Her grandmother creaks up to clear the plates, the shell of the cake. He moves to help, another thing he's learned. She smiles her diluted smile, he reflects it. In the kitchen, he scrapes crumbs into the composter, she rinses the coffee cups. Wanders into a story.

'I was a refugee too, you know. Did she tell you? It was just after the war.' People here use the definite article as if their war was the only one. 'We lived in Pommern. What's now Poland. My mother, seven brothers. Papa was dead already, a kind of Selbstmord. Volunteered for the front. Killed within a week.'

She is matter-of-fact, the cadence of each sentence identical. 'We lost my smallest brother along the way. After that, Mutti was like a train between stations. Never arriving, just rocking along in the dark.' She turns

113

off the water. 'Hunger is what I remember. And fear. It has a smell in people too, you know. Just like your horses.' He stares straight ahead, grips a dirty fork like an oar. She puts a shaky hand on his wrist, gently dislodges the cutlery, clinks it down in the sink.

'We remember. Some of us. What it's like.'

Pats him on the shoulder, turns to her orderly dishwasher. His fiancée appears in the doorway, taps her wrist where her watch cinches. Tomorrow is a black pelted thing hunched in the snow outside.

\*\*\*

Monday noon, he tells them he converted after seeing Jesus in a dream. A four-legged racehorse Jesus, but he keeps that part to himself. Jesus walked on water. He dreams nightly of drowning.

He passes his record of church attendance to the bureaucrat through sweaty palms. They'd started counting from his very first Sunday. Just in case. A form letter with the pastor's sloping signature. Baptism in a huge municipal swimming pool with dozens of others. The quick chlorine convenience of it fills this blank office with the scent of suspicion.

There is nothing sacred in the simple fact of being a fellow human being. Their question is not, Do you believe? Their question is, Can we believe you?

A cold faith for a cold climate, he could tell them. From five times a day down to once a week. Instead they have him naming apostles, enumerating his prayers, emoting his conversion. Everyone converts chin-deep in fear. It's an old Christian tradition. Even their legendary Martin Luther. Mohannad has memorized the story.

Outside in the waiting room, another anxious man contracts into a thick plastic chair, clutches the new gold-plated cross around his neck, prays with his whole body. Each hearing is a rakat, choreographed, routine, full of buoyant hope.

'What is the name of the 40-day fast before Easter?'

He bites Ramadan off the end of his tongue, utters the single, harsh syllable. 'Lent.' How it feels to live, on borrowed time.

She sits behind him, between her parents, dressed in white. Rises to justify herself. Yes, they met in church. Yes, they're planning to marry. Yes, it happened fast. Sometimes these things blindside you. Bombs come screaming out of the clear blue sky.

And then you wait.

\*\*\*

His silenced cell phone lights up the dim aqua stairwell of the Foreigner Registration Office. They stand pressed together, Teutonically optimistic, quietly outraged. The decision will take another four weeks. More black words burned into white paper. Warten. The German word for wait is as familiar to him now as his own name.

He taps the lit screen. The cadence of the Pashtun in the top bunk echoes.

'It's Rahim.' His voice flat as old maps of the earth. 'They put him on a list. Under surveillance. They're searching the room. You'd better come.'

He dreams the gilded Quran wedged into the back corner of his drawer in the dresser. The only thing he'd taken from his brother's listing house. Not because his family had been particularly religious, just because the three charred bodies buried under the single molar of a blank makeshift gravestone had to stay behind. For months he'd clenched the pages of that holy book between the whites of his teeth to keep from grinding himself to dust.

He hangs up, surrounded by expectant faces.

'I have to go.'

Her hopeful smile slips. He feels her hand heavy on his arm, the weight of that ring. Sees her mouth move, hears nothing. Only the steady press of water on his eardrums, the motor of his own heartbeat. Says loudly, too loudly,

'I have to go home. I have to go. I have to.'

HESSE PHILLIPS

# The Way of the Pack

You worry about your daughter. You worry about the fact that she is almost eleven and still walks upstairs on all fours. When she comes home from school she drops her bag by the door, kicks off her sneakers and gets down on her hands and knees with the dogs, barks and yaps and whimpers as though she'd sloughed her humanity off at the threshold. She isn't 'special,' not like that. She's bright. She draws astonishingly realistic pictures of animals. She reads the books your husband left behind in the garage, and her favorites are Jack London and Rudyard Kipling. She watches nature shows instead of cartoons. She knows everything there is to know about wolves, and lectures about them with the competence of a trained zoologist. In the car on the way to school, she tells you, 'Pack structures are hierarchical. There's always an alpha pair at the top and a scapegoat at the bottom. Every member of the pack serves a purpose. The purpose of the scapegoat is to suffer.'

You worry because the principal's office calls you in the middle of the day and suggests an urgent meeting: 'He can see you at 2:30.'

'I have to work,' you say. You are the only mom who works, it seems. The only single mom in the district. There's another kid who gets dropped off every morning in a limousine.

'Well,' says the secretary, 'I suppose we could work out something special for you. Tomorrow at 5?' You don't like the idea of needing special dispensation. You ask what the meeting is about and the secretary turns cagey, puts on a cheerful gloss: 'I'll just let the principal tell you about it.'

Recently, after much cajoling from you, your daughter joined the school chorus, which sometimes meets after hours in the church just up the road. As you drive to pick her up from practice you pray that all is going well, that she enjoys herself, makes a friend or two. When she comes out of the church she bounces into the front seat of your husband's old truck and babbles on about the concert at the end of term, and about the watermelon party the instructor has planned for afterwards, and about the other kids in chorus with her. She speaks of them categorically: the sopranos, mezzos, and altos. She sings snatches of the songs they are learning – 'Chariots of Fire' and 'Memory' – and she seems happy. She

116

seems interested in something human, something that people do and not animals, which gives you hope.

But as soon as she gets home she becomes the little wolf-pup again. Down on all fours, growling and wrestling with the dogs. When bedtime comes around she bounds upstairs on all fours, crawls into bed and curls up as if, swear to God, she had a tail to wrap over her nose. In the middle of the night, you are jolted awake by her howling. Softly at first, but then louder, as if searching for a signal, until the dogs at the foot of your bed start howling too. Exhausted, you find yourself banging on the wall with your fist the way your husband used to do: 'Knock it off!'

The next day at five o'clock you enter the principal's office with a ball of worry in your throat. You are too polite to skip the niceties, of which there are many. Your daughter's chorus instructor is there, her home-room teacher, the principal and his secretary. Your daughter is sitting alone on the floor of the waiting-area just on the other side of the door, playing with little plastic animals, the halls of the school dark beyond that white box of light.

The home-room teacher says, 'We were unaware of this behavior before, because there are no stairs in the school.'

'How often has she done it?' you ask no one in particular.

The chorus-instructor says, 'Every time we go into the church.' You don't like this woman. She has a pinched expression, as though she'd like to hold her nose. As though your daughter smells like dog to her.

'Well,' you say, 'I'll talk to her about it.'

But in the car on the way home, you say nothing, only watch your daughter out of the corner of one eye, watch her like a scientist in a blind, perfectly silent, perfectly still, looking for behaviors to jot in your notebook. She has a whole pack of little plastic wolves in her lap, balanced upright on her thighs, and they scramble around in studied patterns: the cubs with the alpha pair, and the beta wolves all chasing around another wolf, one your daughter has colored black with a magic marker. The betas turn the black wolf belly-up, and he whimpers and writhes. But the others are relentless. They nip and bite until he flees and the other wolves bound after him, happily, before eventually taking him down again, one mashing his throat with open jaws, another tearing at his belly as if to tear it open. This is your daughter, you realize, this quiet, tiny ball of violence, of nature red in tooth and claw. You worry so much. You wonder if you ought to be afraid for her, or *of* her.

'Sometimes the pack kills the scapegoat,' she explains later, sullenly, when you ask her about it over spaghetti.

You put your head in your hands. Then you look up, trying to smile.

117

'Why would they do that?' you ask in a mild, neutral tone. 'Isn't he one of their friends?'

'He's part of the pack.'

'But why would they kill one of the pack?'

She shrugs. 'It's just the way. It's what the scapegoat is there for.'

'Well, that makes no sense to me. What's the point of the scapegoat? He eats with all the other wolves, doesn't he?'

'No. He eats the scraps.'

'Well,' you say, trying to construct a kid-friendly argument, 'maybe the scapegoat needs to learn to stick up for himself. He shouldn't let those bullies boss him around.'

'The scapegoat doesn't fight back. That's not his place.'

'Then what *is* his place?'

Your daughter shrugs again. She eats a meatball with her face close to the bowl and speaks after swallowing, red around the corners of her mouth: 'To keep the pack together. Every wolf is important in the pack. Even the scapegoat. If they don't keep to their place, the pack falls apart.'

'That's not how it should be!' you say, harsher than intended.

'It's the way of the pack,' she says. 'If you were a wolf, you'd understand.'

At bedtime you tell her about the stairs. 'Only in the house, okay?' you say. She agrees, but you aren't sure if she understands why this is so important. You aren't sure you understand why either. You want her to think happy thoughts, human thoughts, about the big concert coming up and the watermelon party, about going out to buy her a new white blouse and a black skirt for the performance. You goad her into talking about the other kids in chorus: Jessica and Jeremy, the popular kids who are most definitely 'going with' each other, and Jeremy's friends Mike T. and Mike Z. and Ryan and Jimmy, and Jessica's friends Valerie and Pamela and Kasey and Kelly and Amy and Beth.

'Will they be at the watermelon party too?' you ask, for her eyes light up whenever you mention it. Your daughter doesn't get invited to a lot of parties.

'Yes,' she says, and gushes about how things will be. They'll eat watermelon on the playground instead of going to second period. She'll swing on the swings. She'll go down the slide. Maybe they'll sing their chorus songs together. She seems to understand, instinctively, the high that comes after a performance. You wonder if maybe she'll get into acting someday. It feels good to think of her in the future tense, becoming a person, becoming a *real* girl. A girl who goes to parties, who likes theatre and music and going shopping for new clothes. Who eats watermelon on the playground with her friends. You need to stop the worry, just for a little while. You need her to be okay. You need to pay the mortgage. You need to hire a divorce lawyer. You don't have the money for either.

You kiss her goodnight. She licks your nose.

On the day of the concert, and of the possibly even more important watermelon party, you drop your daughter off at school with her performance outfit in a dry-cleaning bag on a hanger. 'Put it in your locker and don't let it get dirty,' you say. On this last week before summer, children run up and down the sunbaked sidewalk, crashing into clusters of friends, whimpering and nudging and squealing. And there stands your daughter, alone but beaming, holding the door of your husband's truck open with the new outfit over her arm, looking only at you. 'Bye Mommy. I love you.' And for a moment your worry swells into something bigger, something that nearly stops your heart. It's terror, you think. Or maybe it's love.

'I love you too, baby,' you say.

You cannot attend the concert because you have to work, and your daughter has been wonderfully understanding about this. Perhaps she'll be less understanding once she sees that every other mother in the school is there, because of course they don't work; a school event scheduled for eleven o'clock in the morning on a Friday is no trouble for them. But you have to spend the day sitting at your desk in the hospital's billing office until 2:45, when you are allowed to rush over to the school, pick up your daughter, and rush back with her to finish the workday. While your daughter is singing 'Chariots of Fire' in her new white blouse and black skirt, you are wielding your big red stamp, 'DELINQUENT,' and stuffing envelopes that will go out into the world and ruin someone's day, envelopes that you must lick with your own tongue one after another after another. Your penance for being a part of such cruelty.

You go on a coffee break and the coffee tastes like adhesive. When you return to your desk there's a pink 'While You Were Away' note atop your pile of envelopes waiting to be stuffed.

*SCHOOL CALLED. URGENT.*

After you hang up the phone with the principal's secretary, you run to the car and drive recklessly. The school is twenty minutes from the hospital but you make it there in ten. You don't even bother to park, just skid to a stop at the edge of the playground, hop over the low hedges and sprint across the blacktop towards the edge of the woods, where the children are gathered noisomely in their fresh white tops and black bottoms, along with the chorus instructor and the secretary. At one end of

119

the blacktop stands a long table covered in half-hollowed-out watermelon carcasses, the tablecloth dripping at one corner. As you run you crush broken bits of watermelon rinds underfoot. Seeds and pulp burst over the asphalt. In the grass you trip over several more pieces, slippery and hard at the same time, staining your hospital shoes pink.

'Where is she?' you demand of the adults.

The chorus instructor, with the same sour face as before, points you down a slope of exposed dirt, into the woods. 'In there. I'm not going back there. I nearly got bit!'

Some of the children are still flinging watermelon rinds into the trees.

'Freak!'

'Animal!'

'*Dog!*'

'For God's sake stop it!' you say. For a moment they do. You skid down the slope, wheeling your arms. Halfway down the hill something solid and wet strikes you in the back of the head, so hard you see a flash of white and stop, stunned. Sticky slime dribbles down the back of your neck. You hear a rush of panic come over the pack of kids on the hill above. 'Oh shit! Oh shit, run!' they yell. By the time you turn around, they already have, and the secretary with them.

The chorus instructor remains poised on the crest of the hill with her arms folded. 'Well what do you expect *me* to do?' she whines.

You descend into the thickening trees. Decades ago, when you attended school here, the woods had seemed much larger. Running away from school during recess would have been easy, but you and the other kids had all policed yourselves with stories about wild animals in the woods: coyotes, bob-cats, rabid raccoons. You can't help but wonder if going into the woods is still an act of enormous transgression, the sort of thing only done by the very foolhardy, brave, or desperate.

Just twenty feet into the woods, you find your daughter against the base of a large tree, quivering on all fours. Her new white blouse is pink with watermelon juice. The hair that you combed and pinned this morning hangs loose and dripping about her face, her lip is swollen and bleeding, her cheek bruised, her eyes rounded white, streaming with tears. If she had fur it would be flat against her spine, her tail would be between her legs, her ears flattened against the scruff of her neck.

You know this posture: *I surrender. I surrender. I surrender.*

The animal in you recognizes it before the human does.

GEMMA REEVES

# Fermented

They refer to it as The Meat Joint, never an abattoir. It is a local, small-scale operation processing the red and fallow deer that roam the park. Ten men and two women work there; Joe is the youngest. He often considers the faces of his colleagues, the deep-set lines in their foreheads, the crow's feet reaching for their ears – all the weather and all the hedonism right there on the surface – and cannot imagine being so old and still doing this job. Still doing battle with something already dead.

He has fifteen minutes before he has to leave for work, so he piles a plate with fermented vegetables scooped from his latest jar. Carrots, celery, red onions tumble out. A beetroot stain flowers across the white porcelain. He spears a wedge, sucks the bright vinegar. He can taste white, black, and pink peppercorns. It livens his mouth with a pleasant burn. He rubs his belly. Breakfast of champions, he thinks. He'd almost quit work a few months back, but then Ray turned up. It was Ray who had given him the book about fermenting vegetables, pressed it into his hand after shift one evening. 'For the IBS,' he'd said, and clapped a hand on his back. 'You'd be amazed at how diet can help. No more farting for you, kid.' Ray was right. Joe's stomach had settled; there were fewer desperate dashes to the loo. It was a small, sanitary miracle. He has since mastered sauerkraut, learned how to forage the dandelion flowers and nettles that grow around Sheringham Park. Lately he's interested in kohlrabi, a kind of bastard cabbage. The Google images are intriguing: bumpy green exterior like a malformed apple, round thick base from which leafy stems sprout haphazardly. He has read it tastes like radish, like fennel. He imagines it is a perfect vegetable to ferment – what pleasure, to turn something so crisp into something tangy.

He arranges a few carrots onto a slice of rye bread and chomps. This batch, made with all the veg he knows Ray likes, is finally good enough to share. A thank-you gift. He wraps muslin around the lid of the jar, secures it with brown string, and then nestles it into a Tesco's bag-for-life. He imagines Ray enjoying them at his own kitchen table. But as he realises Jane would be next to him too, the pleasing image curdles.

The morning light is unsure of itself as it tries to filter through the window. It turns the kitchen pale purple; the white units his mum lovingly

121

polishes with lemon spray are glowing. She won't be up for a couple more hours and this allows him, for a short while, to pretend he lives by himself. He wants a leather headboard, a 42-inch telly, and enough cupboard space for all his jars. He would like a flatmate, someone to chill with, watch nature programmes. He despises his mum's thongs hanging out to dry around the house.

He takes his plate to the sink and tackles the washing up. Beetroot juice turns the foam into candyfloss peaks. From the small round window he can see lilac light spreading across the flat Norfolk plains, shaping them in a way that is almost deceptive. Somewhere in the direction of the forest an owl hoots. Five minutes left before he needs to leave for work.

His red Ford Fiesta crunches over the pebbled path in front of the bungalow that his mum refers to as the driveway. He tries not to crush any of the daffodils that have sprung up in defiance of the still-frosty weather. On the passenger seat is an empty Fillet o'Fish box, a McFlurry carton, and a can of energy drink. He takes a moment to look at them regretfully; a deluge of tasty snacks that had his stomach in knots for hours after. Was it worth it? With his left hand he pushes the rubbish out of view onto the scuzzy carpet and makes a mental note to clean the car later. This is a thought he has several times a week. The jar of fermented vegetables is safe on the back seat.

He passes a few blank-eyed houses set back from the road, wisteria coming to life, clipped hedges, ochre-branched willows. He slows as he crosses the bridge and looks into the shallow water's reach, the trees reflected. There are no other cars.

It's only a ten-minute drive, and in that time he vapes zealously, blowing the cherry-flavoured smoke through an open window, blasting the heater to keep warm. As he approaches the park, the arable land and pasture undulates gently. Saw Mill Lake is to his left. If he'd been born two hundred years ago, he'd have ended up working in the mill, providing timber for the estate. He'd enjoyed DT in school, liked how the grain patterns and knots of wood looked like space-probe photos of storms on Jupiter. Magic. Most of his schoolmates fled Roughton the minute they turned eighteen. Off in search of fitter women, better-paid jobs, higher grade MDMA. He blamed his mum, not wanting to leave her alone. But now he is twenty-three, she has a boyfriend much nicer than his dad ever was, and he still hasn't left.

He drives over the cattle ramp and into the estate. Oak trees line the road and a mix of farmland and manicured grounds surround him. From here he can see the speckles on a fallow deer buck shine in the morning light, a strand of bracken caught in his antlers. The rest of the herd are further from the road, clustered around a sweet chestnut.

The Meat Joint is ahead – wide and squat and house-dust grey. Its bleakness intensifies the colour of its surroundings. Ferns seem dragon-green; drifts of snowdrops like a lake of frost. The only windows belong to the adjacent office, a place where guests, or a feared environmental health representative might be invited. Mostly it is where the bosses do the books – Death Admin, Ray calls it. He pulls into the car park and Ray is already there, idling in the clot of weeds by the antler-adorned entrance, back against brick, sucking on a B&H Blue. He blows out cigarette smoke as if he is disgusted with it, as if he is propelling the prospect of cancer away from him. He's wearing the pair of stonewash Levis that are too short for his long legs. A cluster of hairs peaks out between sock and jean, dark and curling. Joe briefly allows himself to imagine the hairs elsewhere on his body, and shivers.

'All right, matey,' Ray says, and claps him on the back before launching into an anecdote about his weekend – something to do with Jane so Joe switches off. Ray likes to talk, and as he does his body emits an energy Joe still finds unfamiliar. Maybe Ray is so good at handling the animals because of this incessant talking, the lilt of his voice must soothe the deer. No one knows quite where he's from except that he did a stint as a chef in a London restaurant. He says he grew up all over, moving around wherever his dad's work took him. No mother. Joe keeps returning to this phenomenon. What would it have been like to have a dad? He senses his mum has made him too emotional. The way he can't look the animals in the eye, even though they are dead and he is alive and in control. The way he can tell himself this over and over but the fact refuses to yield and he still can't look.

'The salty foam was amazing,' Ray is saying. 'I've never tasted anything like it. Made the haddock feel like it'd leapt right from the sea and into my gob. Fresh as. Birdo liked the place, too.' He rests an arm behind his head and leans against the brick.

'Oh cool. You out the dog house, then? Joe asks, scuffing his trainer into the ground, tightening his grip on the Tesco's bag.

'Jane's chilled since the Michelin Star restaurant. Forgave everything. I know what ladies need,' he says, and scratches the brown stubble on his left cheek. 'Let me teach you a thing or two when we're next in the pub. You should be putting it about at your age, mate.'

'Yeah,' Joe says and looks at the ground again.

Ray's mouth opens and closes as he inhales smoke and then exhales. Joe watches the birthmark that straddles Ray's bottom lip and chin. It is purple-pink and flares more toward one shade or the other, mood-dependent. On his animated days, it is strawberry and looks as a kid might after carelessly eating a fistful of the fruit. When he's aggravated, it matches the blackberry wine Ray brews in his garage and brings to work in green glass bottles. The wine is sweet and potent and stains teeth and tongues a mysterious shade of purple. Joe picked blackberries with his dad when he was still around. When he drinks the wine and touches the pads of his thumbs, he can feel the brambles of the blackberry bush prick the soft flesh, can see the red scratches that would stay for a week.

Ray finishes his cigarette and spits on the ground and the glob is enormous, a lone jellyfish. It is both disgusting and fascinating to see something like that come out of Ray's mouth.

Joe opens the door and lets Ray walk ahead of him into the glare of fluorescent strip lighting. He knows Phil and Gareth are already there because the building is vibrating with the techno the brothers both favour. Their heyday was nineties acid house and this is how they run The Meat Joint. Saws, blades, rave music. It almost covers the sound of chains rattling, machines clanking. Sometimes he finds it difficult, watching them throwing shapes around the carcasses, clacking chewing gum.

He and Ray dump their phones and jackets in the lockers. They cover their jeans, hoodies, and trainers with oversized transparent white jackets, blue hairnets and boot covers. Ray is still talking about food.

'I've got something for you, actually,' Joe finally says, pulling protective chain mail over his jacket. 'Remember that book you gave me about fermenting? Well it really helped, actually. So I made you a batch. It's my best yet.' He takes the jar out of the Tesco bag and holds it, nervously, in front of him. Ray looks at the jar.

'You did, mate? That's lovely, that is. Lovely. What a treat.'

Joe grins, relieved, and is about to hand over the veg when Greg appears. He hides the jar behind his back.

'Oi mate,' Ray says to Greg. 'You owe me a pint or seven. Jane came back from tea with yer wife yesterday, and all she could talk about was babies. Had to have meself a whisky to calm down.'

Greg laughs. 'Just let it happen,' he says. 'You don't really have to do much 'til they start walking anyway. All they want is boob.'

'Isn't that all everyone wants?' Ray smirks, as he slips his stocky hands into thick brown leather gloves, salutes Joe, and heads towards the Care Area with Greg.

'See you,' Joe calls out to his back. He is still holding the jar. He stores it in the locker, puts on chainmail gloves and studies his silver hands for a moment. He'll give the veg to Ray at break.

In the De-Boning room, Gillian nods hello and Meg says, 'Hiya darling.' He's always on time but those two make a point of being early.

He likes them but is baffled by the pride they take in their work, how they brag in the pub. When his mates come back to Roughton, they call him Killing Machine, and Death Dude. They don't understand what he does. Why should they? – a trainee estate agent, a bank clerk, a personal trainer. The Meat Joint is the forgotten part of the supply chain. The bit no one likes to think about – the missing link between farm and kitchen. Phil and Gareth have made it so that they measure the meat in units of production, not bodies. This helps him deal with the immense carcasses he's not strong enough to lift – an embarrassment that lives in him, bubbling as a thought that contaminates him several times a day. Usually, no one works in the same room for long. The intensity forces them to switch it up. But for three years he's managed to avoid the Hot Room. He knows what happens there. He knows it intellectually, can imagine each sequence of events, even dreams of it sometimes. Skinned and split deer pass at head height, hanging from hydraulic hooks on the overhead haulage system. Gravity expels the offal and entrails, a puff of steam when the warmth of the beast's interiors hit the cold exterior of the floor. The redundant organs fill his nostrils with an acrid stench.

In the air-conditioned De-Boning Room he makes the cut, divides the meat, turns the whole into parts. Loin, heart, ribs. He is The Meat Joint's prize de-boner. Precise with his work, the small slender fingers he was teased about at school are nimble and efficient. He is lauded for his attention to detail. Rhythm is key. Begrudgingly, he knows the music helps but really he is tuning in to a calm hum somewhere inside of him. He slips a nose plug in to escape the smell of zinc. With a gloved hand he touches the beast's open body, feels the cold pocket of inert tissue, the lifeless muscle, and cuts. It is both practical and cruel that the walls inside are white, that the tiles never stay clean.

At break he goes outside to vape. His eyes are strained from concentrating; his ears are ringing. The duff duff duff of techno still makes him nervy, keeps him suspended in the same feeling he used to get before dropping a pill in a club – simultaneous intensity and restraint, wanting to control the impending high. It has turned into a beautiful day. The blue of the sky deepening across the park makes The Meat Joint look less brooding. Half a dozen cigarette butts defile the flowerbed Meg optimistically planted and half-heartedly tends. He pulls out his vape, switches the cherry cartridge for blueberry sherbet.

He checks his watch, wonders why Ray hasn't come on break yet.

Across the way, Phil and Gareth are drinking Kenco in Styrofoam cups and talking in hushed tones. Nearly in their fifties, the brothers are only a year apart and each mirror the other: pale eyes, loose grey skin, rivers of detonated capillaries running across their cheeks, silver flecked hair cropped close to the skull. Gareth is balding at a slightly faster rate. Despite spending their youth burning brain cells they are utterly turgid, square of chest. He suspects steroids. But both men look exhausted. The demand for venison has tripled in recent years, mostly due to being marketed as the healthier option for red meat lovers. Joe hasn't eaten meat in two years.

Dave from the Hot Room arrives and pulls out a half-eaten pack of gingernuts. He wields the stun gun and is the kind of de-sensitised old-timer that horrifies the newbies. He casts an eye in the direction of Phil and Gareth, turns back to Joe and raises a brow.

'They're so effing serious these days,' Dave says.

Joe grunts in the affirmative.

'It used to be much easier,' Dave continues. 'All this blinking red tape, piles of paperwork, all this concern for *animal welfare*,' he says, rolling his eyes and making air quotes with his fingers. 'There's a reason we're at the top of the food chain, you know?'

Joe nods. This kind of mild grumbling slips from Dave's mouth about once a week. He does not get on with the new breeds like Meg and Gillian, uni graduates who work to a formula, ticking all the boxes. Also, they are women, which is even more unforgiveable than being educated.

'Hey kid,' Phil says. 'Come here.'

He approaches Phil with caution. Since Foot and Mouth, many of the small abattoirs have shut down and Phil struts around having not only made it through the crisis, but also increased the demand. The workload is such that sometimes they have to turn away livestock. All in all, Phil is insufferably smug.

'Greg's wife has gone into labour early,' Phil says. 'He's gotta dash off. You need to go help Ray herd in the livestock.'

Joe says nothing. Attempts to stare down Phil. Fails. 'But I've never done that,' he says.

'I know kid. I'm your boss. I'm telling you to go help. Get rid of that chain mail, scrub off, then hot-foot-it to the Care Area. Ray'll show you what's what. It's not hard.'

Joe turns to Gareth and uses his eyes to appeal the decision. Gareth just nods.

'Can't someone else?' he tries again, and what he means by that is, I can't do it, I can't do it, I can't look them in the eye even when they're dead.

'No son,' Gareth says. 'You're up.' At least he'll be there with Ray.

At the lockers he checks his phone. His mate Rob has sent him a video of a cat ice-skating. He lifts the chain mail from his shoulders and tips his body over until gravity does the work for him. A pool of sweat gathers at the small of his back. His stomach knots in the familiar way. He takes out the jar of fermented veg.

In the bathroom, the antibacterial soap globs out from the steel dispenser. He scrubs all the way up his arms, avoids looking in the mirror.

He knows they play panpipe music to relax the deer, but as he enters the Care Area he is taken aback nonetheless. He cannot believe the sound. It is so soft and so airy and there is Ray, humming along to an instrumental *My Heart Will Go On*, brushing the lustrous coats. Straw covers the concrete floor, drains and hosepipes in-between the configured pen runs. But it is calm in here, how he imagines a spa to be. Joe looks at the deer and then he looks at Ray, crooning along to the melody of the panpipes. He has a lovely voice. Please stop singing, he thinks. He looks back at the deer. So beautiful. The animals should never sense imminent death. If the beast freaks, shock hormones race through its blood stream, through every nerve, and later appear as a ripple in the cut of meat like a wodge of superglue across a once-broken vase. But he knows exactly what will happen when they get them around that corner. The anatomical drawing of the head, the precise point of the brain marked with a felt tip black cross. And after the stun gun, Dave will lift the eyelids and touch the eyeball to check if the deer is dead. The trap door below the animal opens and it drops down to the Hot Room. He looks at the beasts and then he looks at Ray.

He's drawn to the deer. How they bow and then raise their necks. The colour of their hide is like flamed maple, like spruce. How is it that he's never noticed they are the colour of the forest? They're magnificent.

Ray strokes the haunch of the next one to be herded round the corner. Joe cannot believe how gentle he is. How nice it must be to be stroked that way. The deer looks like it could swagger back into the park if it wanted, but instead its strong muscular tongue licks Ray's hand. He cannot believe it. Did he imagine it?

He approaches Ray with the jar of fermented vegetables grasped in his brown-gloved hand and instead of saying – Hey mate, come to join you. Can't believe Greg's missus is dropping so early. You gonna show me the ropes then? What's first? Or even – Here, I brought the veg for you, something to snack on since you missed your break. No. Instead he says nothing and very slowly comes behind Ray and he leans into the curve of his body and gently kisses the side of his face, just above the birthmark on his chin.

He does not taste strawberries – just salt.

When Ray hits him, it is hard, catching his left cheekbone with fat knuckles. Warm blood flows from his nose and back into his mouth, which is open, gasping. He is struck by the peculiar sensation of feeling something long hidden inside of him spurt out only to return inside again. The body is marvellous, he thinks briefly. The jar shoots from his hands and shatters. The vegetables look ridiculous strewn across the ground. The brine seeps into the straw. He shuts his eyes and recognises the opening bars of *(Everything I Do) I Do it For You* breathy and hushed over the tannoy. But the deer are no longer calm, they're sniffing, a strong deep sound, and a bad bad sign. And then they begin to lightly stomp their hooves. It sounds like a wood block striking the ground. Ray grasps the collar of his jacket. He smells of sweat and hay, a pleasing combination. There is another blow, and his ribs ricochet against Ray's knee. He feels the languid sweep of his own left arm before cold dirt floor meets cheek. Rising above his own hacking and spluttering is the sound of the deer snorting, sensing danger. When he vomits it is pink and for a moment he thinks it must be blood but then he remembers the beetroot at breakfast. He clutches his belly, senses a boot imprint on the flesh. Men's voices from somewhere above him join the racket. He can't distinguish them from the beat of a baseline. There's a throbbing pain behind his right eye. He tries to catch his breath. He rolls onto his hands and knees, lets Ray pummel his body, feels it flung back and forth, back and forth, like a piece of flotsam on a wave's break. But inside he is charged with a kind of electricity, all nerve endings twitching like a balloon rubbed across hair. The deer snorts grow louder and louder. He recalls mating season, the bucks' short deep grunts as they find the doe they desire and claim their territory. The bounding legs of the doe as she runs away. He wonders if the men will assume he'd asked for it. If they'll know he wanted the contact.

AMY STEWART

# Wolf Women

If Una screams as loudly as she could, no one would hear her. She thinks about this often. The woods swallow things: sound, time, the person she was when she lived in the city. John owned a cabin deep in the North Shore mountains, and it was his idea to move here permanently. So, they've swapped grubby high-rises for fir-clad hillside, eye-level gloom, long, empty mornings of mist and birdsong. John travels to the closest town every night to work in a bar, sleeps all day. Una tends to the chickens and makes wooden chopping boards to sell at the market. There is a family of racoons she likes to watch; they emerge at dusk with reassuring regularity, scavenging where she leaves out peelings and scraps.

There are things she misses. Friends, casual meetings arranged only an hour prior and edged with a fuzziness of white wine. Streets of people jostling for space, sharing air. This lonely landscape scares her sometimes. It shocks her into alertness with its lack of pretension – a yellow leaf is simply a yellow leaf, as startling and colourful as it seems, an animal's eye is unbearably open and staring. There is no subtext, no manmade ambiguity. She can't ignore it or explain it away. It has an edge of malice, Una thinks, this honesty; the stark and uncompromising intensity of the natural world. It seeps through and invades her life subtly but surely – the front porch is never free of crunching leaves or scattered needles, and she trips over dead rats in the garden. But John is happy here, and that makes her life easier. Just me and you, he says. No one to bother us up here. Una nods as though she's grateful, as though he's taught her something important. Although sometimes, just sometimes, Una wishes that someone would bother them.

The woman arrives on a rainy Monday evening as it's getting dark. John's just left for work and Una's washing up. There's a face at the window, pale and moon-like. Una gasps and drops a plate, sending it shattering on the floorboards.

'Fuck,' she whispers, her hands rushing up out of the water, dripping with soap suds.

The woman barely reacts. She looks to be in her late teens or early twenties, with wide, clear eyes and a scattering of honey freckles on makeup-free skin. Her clothes and hair are sodden, though from her blank expression she doesn't seem to care, or notice. She's cradling her forearm, which is wrapped in a strip of grey fabric. 'Sorry to disturb you,' she says. Her voice is thin and reedy through the glass. 'I managed to fall and cut myself while hiking. Do you mind if I come in to clean up a little?'

Una has a low, rumbling feeling, like an egg cracking in the pit of her stomach. She ignores it – she's brought her city paranoia with her. Life is simpler out here, and there are plenty of hiking trails around. The woman gives her an apologetic smile. 'I've scared you. I'm sorry.'

Politeness makes Una shake her head. 'No, it's fine. Just a second.' She removes her gloves with a peeling suck and unlocks the door. As soon as the woman's over the threshold, her shoulders slope a little. She rolls her neck and it clicks once, twice. Una can't put her finger on how, but the woman's demeanour changes. She's taking in the wooden farmhouse-style kitchen as though she's been waiting a long while to see it.

'How bad is the cut? I'll get the TCP,' Una offers.

The woman ignores her. 'Can I have some apple pie? I've been hiking for hours.'

Una laughs in surprise, though her skin prickles. 'Well, I actually made some yesterday. That's... funny. Give me a minute.'

The woman is non-plussed. Her hair sprays water onto the floor as she shakes herself off, unselfconscious and dog-like. Una feels herself being watched as she opens the fridge, cuts a slice of pie, plates it. She sets it down on the counter and goes to retrieve the TCP and some cotton wool from the bathroom. When she returns, the woman is attacking the pie with fervour, dusty crumbs lining her lips. There'll be none left, but John doesn't like Una to eat much, anyway.

'Thank you,' the woman mumbles. 'I can't remember the last time I ate.'

'Right. No problem.' Una blots some TCP onto a pad and offers it to the woman, who ignores it. Hairs stand up on Una's forearms, summoned by a strangeness she can't define. 'So,' Una says, feigning casualness. 'Do you live nearby?'

'Not particularly.' When the woman is finished with the pie, she pushes the plate aside and drags a sleeve across her mouth. 'Got any Pop Tarts?'

Una blinks. She starts to think there might be something wrong with the woman. She's wearing an oversized hoodie that almost reaches her knees, black leggings scattered with holes. There's dirt on her neck and up to her ears, and Una expects the unwashed odour to fill the kitchen – but there's only dampness and perhaps the faint memory of perfume. The woman tilts her head, like an animal awaiting instruction. John would never have let her in. Confident words stutter and die in Una's throat, leaving only, 'Um, no. No Pop Tarts, sorry. Now about that cut...'

The woman gives her a sly smile. 'Lying,' she whispers, and it makes the skin at the back of Una's neck tingle. 'I was being polite. You've got chocolate ones in that cupboard,' her head inclines to the one above the stove, 'there.'

Una's throat constricts painfully, and they stare at each other in silence. The rain's picked up a little. It always rains like the ground is parched out here; fat drops patter through upturned leaves, turning the tree roots slick and obscuring the lines between path and undergrowth. It raises the spirits of smells from the forest floor. It's loud now, drumming like Una's pulse. Something red flutters outside the window and Una realises she's left the washing out. John will be furious. She needs to go and get it, but she can't move.

'Who are you?' she asks the woman quietly. 'What do you want?'

The woman sighs, eyes shifting up to the ceiling, like a petulant child. 'I've told you. Pop Tart.' She slowly unwinds the strip of fabric around her arm and discards it on the floor with a wet slop. There's nothing under it, nothing but creamy white skin.

Una stands, galvanised by fear. 'I'd like you to leave. Please.'

The woman's thin lips quirk. Her eyes are as shiny as coins. 'My name is Jane,' she says simply. 'And something horrible is going to happen to you, I can smell it. I'm here to help you.'

Una inhales sharply. Her brain begins to whir. Something her sister had told her before she and John left the city. Emma came over to help her pack, and after half-heartedly filling some boxes, they'd drunk beer and watched TV. The news had been covering the most recent in a spate of attacks on men. A nightclub owner, tied to a lamp post, his fingers cut off.

'And you wonder why John wants to get out of the city?' Una said. Emma hadn't approved of the move, or of John, and Una had hoped to convince her sister a little of his good character.

'I reckon it's the wolf women,' Emma said through a mouthful of Doritos.

'The *what*?'

'You haven't heard of them? Bit of an urban legend. They're a kind of vigilante group, all calling themselves Jane. They have a... developed sense of smell.'

Una had laughed, turned her nose up in the air like a dog on a hunt. 'I smell you went to the gym before you came over.'

Emma had chuckled but not dropped the subject. 'My friend knows one. She says they can smell thoughts, emotions, desires. Rottenness. They've evolved a kind of second scent, something to do with increased sensory neurons in the nose – they can tell when someone wants to hurt

131

them, so instead they do the hurting. Particularly men, and particularly men who hate women. A couple of guys at work are getting paranoid. They're demanding the police do more.' Emma had hesitated, not met Una's eye. 'As you say. John seems to be in an awful hurry to leave.'

The implications of the remark hurt, but defending John to Emma always ended badly. Instead, Una had said, 'Sounds like guys in trouble trying to cover something up.' She'd changed the channel, forgotten about it. Now she watches as Jane reaches into the top cupboard and takes out the Pop Tarts she'd somehow known were there.

'That's better.' Jane doesn't ask for them to be toasted, just crumbles them up dry and cold, drops them piece by piece into her open mouth like a bird. She barely seems to swallow. Una notices only now that she's barefoot, and she's tracked a pattern of mud across the floor. John won't like that. For all his love of isolation, he doesn't care much for actual wildness.

Jane jerks her head to look at Una. 'Is he nice to you?' she asks.

'Who?'

'The man you're thinking about.'

Una sighs. 'Yes.' She's aware that answer sounds a bit baggy around the edges but she's not thinking straight. Besides, she doesn't owe this woman anything.

'He doesn't smell nice,' Jane says. She sits back down and brings a knee up to her chin. She looks unsubstantial, childish, and Una berates herself for feeling afraid. She just needs to humour the woman, then she'll leave.

'You're one of the wolf women,' Una says carefully. The words are absurd, too big on her tongue. 'How... how does it work? Your gift?'

Jane wrinkles her nose, the lines carving tiger stripes in the skin. 'There aren't real words for the things we smell, and we don't always get the full picture. But your husband... he smells like cleave-meat. Steel-tang. Skulling.' Decisively, as if a clock has struck, she wipes her hands down the front of her clothes and stands. 'You're safe for now, though. I'll be back tomorrow, and we can talk more.'

She makes for the door. Una follows. 'I don't want you to come back.'

Jane shrugs and pulls up her hood. 'I'll tell you why your husband is dangerous – what he's already done. When I come tomorrow.'

*John, dangerous?* The thought is met with hollowness. The rain is still thundering down, and it strikes Una to ask Jane where she's going, but instead she says, 'I might call the police.'

Jane's nostrils twitch. 'You won't.'

The next day, Una's fidgety. She watches the racoons – a protective mother and three clumsy kits – sift through potato peelings and locate what little was left of the apple pie. She hides food under the porch; John wouldn't take kindly to her feeding wildlife. She'd wanted to tell John about Jane when he'd gotten back past midnight, but he'd had a busy shift and was in one of his more sullen moods, nursing a beer in front of sports highlights. They'd sat side by side drinking too much and gone to bed without touching. The language of Una's drunk dreams was filled with Jane's words, and she's still hungover with them today.

The wolf women surely can't be real. Una has to tell John about Jane. She'll do it as soon as he gets back tonight. In the meantime, she cleans, needing something productive to do with her hands. She drives to the bakery a couple of towns over and buys a cherry tart, a chocolate gateau and two cinnamon buns. On the ride home, her car smells warm and sweet.

Una waits. She tells herself she isn't, but she is; she's waiting for Jane. The woman comes later than the previous night, and she's braided some wildflowers into her hair. Now that it isn't wet, Una can see it's the colour of fox fur and hangs in uneven curtains around her strange, staring face. The two women don't greet each other. Jane simply walks in and says, 'I'll take the gateau, please.'

Una feels as though something has shifted dangerously off-kilter as she lays out a fat slice. What is she doing, letting this woman back in her house while she's alone? At least she knows John's shotgun is in the workshop next door. He won't show her how to work it, but she's sure she'd be able to figure it out. It gives her an idea.

'We can talk,' she tells Jane, 'but I need to work.'

Jane shrugs. 'Fine by me.'

The workshop is reassuring in its cool calm, the smell of lemon balm and sanded wood heavy in the air. Here, Una has the upper hand. There's a stack of boards waiting to be oiled in the corner. They're all made from the trees on their property, left outside to warp before being planed in here. These lot are almost ready for market, after she gives them their protective coating. She passes one to Jane.

'You can help,' she says.

'They're beautiful,' Jane whispers. The words are almost tender.

Una shows her what to do, and for twenty minutes or so they work in a silence that's surprisingly companionable. Una keeps wanting to hold Jane to the promise she made yesterday – that she'd tell her what John has done. In the same second, she feels guilty for believing that John has done anything, and that this strange, wild woman would know what it was. So, she stays quiet. She forces herself not to look at Jane. It's not an attractiveness that keeps her glancing over, not exactly – more a *pull*. Jane never stays still. Her movements are staccato as a hummingbird's but somehow graceful, feline. She's quick and skilled with the boards. Una stares at Jane's hands as though they're evidence, trying to figure out if there's potential for violence there. They're surprisingly clean; the nails are short but not bitten. Her fingers are slick with oil.

'It got too risky for us in the city,' Jane says suddenly, without looking up. 'They're rounding up any one who shows a whiff of the gift. A few of us have come out here. I smelt you and your husband and… I thought I'd better come.'

Una takes a breath. 'And you can… you can *smell* John's past – his intentions?' she laughs. Not cruelly, and more to herself. 'You can smell he's dangerous like you can smell a fucking gateau in my fridge? Do you really expect me to believe that?'

Jane sighs. 'Might keep you alive if you did.' The silence returns, heavy and oppressive this time, until Jane breaks it. 'It might be easier to show you.' She puts down the board she's been polishing, stands, and leaves the workshop. Una pauses for a few seconds and then follows. Jane's waiting for her in the hall, and when she sees Una, she takes a few careful steps up the wooden staircase and looks down at her bare feet. 'Here,' she whispers. She begins to pry up the floorboard with deft fingers. Before Una can protest, the board lifts with a creak. It hadn't been properly nailed down. Jane kneels, sniffs, sticks a hand into the cavity.

Una doesn't recognise what she pulls out at first. It looks like hair, heads and heads of it. But then Jane lays whatever it is on the steps and Una can see that it's rope, cascading down the staircase like serpents. It's stained dark red. Una's pulse feels as though it lives in her throat.

'It smells like woman.' Jane says flatly. 'Withering, angry flesh.'

'What…' Una starts, not knowing what she's trying to say. 'Why is that there?'

'It touched a woman he loved once,' Jane tells her, almost sadly. 'He brought her here. As he's brought you, now that he's tired of you.'

The words are a slap across the face. Not because they hurt, but because they don't. Una tries to rationalise. Surely the ropes have been here from before John bought the cabin. Used for animals of some kind.

'He has dark, dark thoughts,' Jane says quietly. 'He doesn't want them.' Her wide eyes flash. She holds up a bloodied rope. Her voice is flat and metallic. 'But that didn't stop him last time.'

***

Una lies in bed, listening to the owls hoot in the trees. She's still shaking even though Jane left hours ago, disappearing into the early twilight like a ghost. She'd left with that same assurance – that Una was safe for now. But she wouldn't be for long. John hasn't returned from the bar yet. The space beside her is freezing, the mattress depressed in the echo of his enormous, powerful body. Una has the terrible feeling, sitting like a stone in her stomach, that he knows Jane has been coming here, and it makes her bones ache with fear. Could he really have killed someone? A woman? She wants to reject the idea with disgust, but it fits like a key in a lock.

She remembers when she'd first met John. She'd been working in a city dive bar. He'd ordered whiskey and they'd talked before closing time. He had a black eye – a fight last night, boys will be boys – but his manner was friendly, relaxed. He had a confidence that swept her up in its ease, and he listened to her with rapt attention.

'Have you ever been married?' she'd asked, loading the dishwasher under the bar. It was a careless question, but he'd met her eye with the unnerving intensity she'd come to know well.

'Yes. But she won't trouble me anymore.'

***

Every night for the next three weeks, Jane appears, apart from on John's nights off. Una never has to tell her when these are. She's beginning to fill out from all the pies Una feeds her, becoming more substantial – cheeks flushed with blood, the curve of her hip more prominent underneath her shapeless hoodie.

They watch the racoons together. The kits are growing larger, bolder, sometimes one or two appear without the mother. One day, the mother stops accompanying them altogether. Una feels a certain responsibility for Jane. Somehow, she's keeping herself safe, relatively clean. But how long can she survive on cake? Is she eating anything else? One night, Una opens the fridge, peers inside. 'Carrot?' she offers.

Jane scrunches up her nose. So instead they feast on Pop Tarts and powdery meringue, bitter coffee cake studded with walnuts and fluffy Victoria Sponge. Jane is unabashed about her gluttony, jam on her gums and sugar underneath her fingernails. Sometimes they talk about John, but mostly their conversations are benign, slow and rambling. They discuss constellations, poisonous plants, the animals calling out in the woods. The nights feel solid and comforting, more real than the days now, when Una dreads the period between John waking and going to work. At least he spends most of his nights off at a friend's, drinking away the hours. She exists in a blurry limbo; terrified of John, but not quite believing he'd ever seriously hurt her. He responds to her standoffishness in kind. When she refuses sex, he doesn't seem particularly perturbed. It's almost a relief to not have to pretend.

One night in early November, Jane doesn't come. Una's bought a cherry tart and ends up eating almost the whole thing by herself, not even bothering with cutlery. Her fingers are stained inky purple. She's getting it all over her clothes, not caring, becoming more and more anxious by the minute. What could have kept Jane?

It's past midnight when Jane's face appears at the window. Her lip is fat, the thin skin fit to bursting. One eye is swollen shut. Una rushes to unlock the door, ushers her inside. 'What happened?' Her voice comes out in a breathy rush.

Jane takes a seat on her usual stool and Una serves her the rest of the pie. Jane doesn't touch the plate. She presses her face tenderly, but more to map the violence than to check if it hurts. She does not wince. 'A man. I was asleep – didn't smell him.' Blood leaks from her lip while she speaks.

Una has been watching her dumbly, feeling Jane's pain as if it lives in her own body. But now she springs into action. She doesn't have long until John gets back. She wets a cloth with warm water and dabs softly at Jane's face. 'We have to call the police,' she says.

Jane jerks away, eyes crackling. 'Police. Who do you think did this?' The ferocity of her voice doesn't sound like it comes from her. She jabs a finger at her own face. 'You think this is bad? You haven't seen what they do to the women who can't fight them off. They don't believe in the gift. They just think we're man-haters; killers of innocents. That's why I came here when I smelt John's intentions, not to the police. What proof do we have?'

Jane's right - there isn't any. You can't show the police the days you spent silent for fear of incurring anger, or the nights you lay awake, terrified of a cold hand on your back – a hand that never asks. You need something physical. Una has an idea. 'The ropes. There'll be DNA on the ropes.'

Jane sniffs the air, chuckles sadly, then hugs her arms around herself. 'Sure. Go and get them, then.'

There's something off about the way she says it, but determination flickers in Una's belly now. She approaches the stairs, tries to remember which board Jane peeled up. Once she finds it, it comes up easily, more easily than before, and her fingers trail the inside. Her hands hit something soft, not rope-like. Something furry but cold. Her stomach twists even before she pulls it out. It's the mother racoon, her strong body sad and limp. Her fur is matted with dried blood on one side. Una resists the urge to drop the animal back inside the hole – instead laying it gently on the step.

Jane is already standing at the bottom of the stairs, and she gives a sad little laugh. 'He knows you know.' She shifts weight off a leg that's bled through her leggings. 'We don't have long.'

\*\*\*

The next morning, Una spits blood into the sink. John had come back late, reeking of whiskey. She'd curled up on the sofa, said she wasn't feeling well. This time, he was not so easily passed off. He'd taken off his belt and lashed it out, just once, laughing almost benevolently while he did it like they were trying something new, and it smacked hard against her face. There's an angry streak across her mouth this morning, like a lipstick smudge. Something's shifted. Something huge. Something she can't put back.

John sleeps all day and leaves for work early without acknowledging her, and so Jane arrives early too. For the first time, Una sees her in natural light. Her one open eye shines an iridescent amber. The lid of the other is turning purple; her fat lip beginning to crust. She isn't surprised to see Una's own marred face. For once, she shakes her head when Una offers her food.

'It smells sad and heavy in here. Let's go outside.'

Una follows Jane down a winding dirt path that skirts the densest part of the woods. It smells like forest, low and warm. They walk slowly, Jane jumping nimbly where Una stumbles. They come to a shrubby meadow, flecked with violet wildflowers. The grasses sway in a half-hearted breeze, flaring rose gold in the fading light. The meadow is ringed by grand Douglas Firs that watch over them like sentinels. Jane sits, and Una follows. The grass creates a soft bed, and they both lie down, bone-tired. Neither has the energy to speak for a long time. Una's mouth throbs. She closes her eyes, listens to the day dying. She knows what Jane is going to say before she says it.

'It's time to leave.' Her words are like dandelion seeds floating in the wind. 'He's tired of you. You won't survive the night.'

Una expects her stomach to scrunch up, the muscles to protest. She thinks she should scream. She should cry. Instead, she feels like a dead weight sinking to the bottom of the river, and says simply, 'What shall I do?'

Jane turns to her. A bee buzzes around her face, lands briefly on her bruised cheek, takes off again. 'Go back to the house. Take what you can. Drive back to the city.'

Una nods. She wishes she could stay here, where time feels lazy and stretchy, violence a bad dream. 'And what about you?'

Jane's amber eye glints, the pupil a midnight blade. 'I think I'll stay here for a while.' She turns her face to the sun. Una has a sudden urge for her skin to touch Jane's. She brings Jane in close to her, presses her face to her chest. Someone watching might see a mother and a child, embracing as the day evaporates like smoke. It's the closest they've ever been. Jane smells like wheat, fire, damp fur. Una has a sense she's losing something; that something is falling away.

They part; Una turning her back on the meadow, Jane lying back in the warm grasses. Una walks through the cooling forest to the cabin and upon reaching it, wavers; how can she leave? How can she believe Jane? Then she remembers the dead racoon, the bloody ropes, the ache around her mouth, and she steels herself. An hour later she emerges from the cabin, throws a case and her best boards from the workshop into the car boot, and is gone. The racoon kits, fully grown now, watch her leave. She vows never to return, although as dirt roads turn to concrete, she does worry about John finding her in the city.

But she doesn't see the female figure that creeps into the cabin once she's gone, wildflowers delicately threaded into her hair. The figure that goes to the workshop, loads John's shotgun and waits. Waits for the darkest hours, for howls to splinter the forest. For a man to return and find that his wife is gone, and that there's a wolf in his house.

NICI WEST

# Crow

When she moved, it slithered inside her like a worm, making its way around her womb, comfortable in her skin. It felt like its beak dug into her spine. A queer stranger had moved in, embedding itself in places it didn't belong, taking possession of her body and calling it home. If she was brave, she could look down and see parts taking shape under her skin like stones under clay, pushed into the lining of her comfy nest and reshaping it. Not ready to come out yet.

She didn't know how long she would be pregnant for. It had grown fast, from its first flutter of a movement in the frozen meat aisle – when she'd been looking at a leg of lamb considering if it was big enough to feed her then husband, brother and mum – to a bump large enough to take up spaces between bodies on public transport. Despite the strange, inconclusive ultra-scans, the doctor wouldn't listen to what she knew.

At strange hours she found herself fighting cravings so strong she convulsed with desire. Salvia filled her tongue. Stomach cramped. In her slippers and nightgown she slipped out the front door, down the cracked stone steps, trod carefully through the neighbour's outdoor porch into the communal garden, the drizzle cool against her calves. The neighbour's cat squawked with desire, on heat and unfazed by her appearance.

The ground was at the back of the garden was where it was muddiest, where it had been a wasteland of litter from the drunk and lazy passers-by just off the main road, until the neighbours had pulled together to get it cleared. Now it sat on an exposed piece of land, fresh mud upturned, waiting for transformation.

She knelt. Slippers hanging loose from her heels. A few forgotten weeds. The pre-pregnant her would have cringed at the feel of dirt on her hands, paused to inspect it getting stuck under her nails. Now she was gripped in desire and she couldn't stop until it had been satisfied. She dug her fingers into the ground. Pushed the loose surface aside. Plunged her other hand deeper, to upturn the softer mud below, pulling loose the worms living in the sodden earth. She took her forefinger and thumb and stole one from its home. It bent and wiggled, pink head catching the light from the street lamps. She held it front of her face, or at least that's what she wanted to do, but instead, her arm moved into her open lips, grit and movement on her tongue. It felt silkier in her mouth than she expected.

It tickled her throat. She chewed.

It had a bite to it, a slight resistance, then softened, lost its shape until it was a mass of dirt and blood and muscle in her mouth. It took a long time to chew, maybe three minutes or so, and the creature inside her started to vibrate and shake with excitement.

\*\*\*

If it was human, it would have made her breasts ready to burst, a heaving sign of nature preparing her body for nurture. It would have grown slowly, over months, small flutterings gradually giving way to tumbles and turns, a feeling no human could describe who hadn't been pregnant. It would have been birthed with muscle and contractions, deep breaths and strained pushes, tiny body almost too big to break free but head subtle enough to be forced into the world.

The birth was anomalous. It happened at six months gestation. She was alone, in her flat, at three in the morning, her bed sheets dirtied with sweat and blankets crushed from tossing and turning. The sensation of the worms from that night still fresh on her tongue. A hot memory. She was wet between the legs but didn't think anything different, her whole body was drenched in sweat and fear. It was only when her contractions started – when it felt like the earth moved and quaked inside her, that her own body had turned against her – that she realised she was in labour. And it was at that moment that she thought about the reality of birthing a crow; would it be small enough, would its beak tear her, would it have feathers? Would she be a good mother? The scattered steady whine of the London sirens called from outside her flat. Her phone vibrated. The unstoppable tide of moving muscles.

\*\*\*

She woke in hospital. Hooked to wires and machinery, surrounded by metal frames, sterile blue curtains and distant voices. It was daylight and the last thing she remembered was being wheeled through the hospital doors on a stretcher, an oxygen mask being pulled over her face, a stranger holding her hand. She felt different somehow. Her body empty.

'He's beautiful,' a nurse said, rolling in a box in that looked like a plastic coffin on wheels, pulling it up next to her bed. Inside: tiny black feathers, small yellow beak, the pink skin over closed eyes. It wiggled.

'He wants you to hold him. Have you got some worms?'

'What?'

'I said time for skin to skin? I'm the duty midwife. Sounds like you've had quite a night.'

She was unclipping the plastic coffin, swaddling the thing in blankets, preparing it for her.

'Will it be able to feel my skin?'

'Of course. It's good for him to feel connected to you.'

'But what about...' She looked down at its yellow beak against the soft pink blanket.

'What?'

*Its feathers*, she thought. A pulse of panic shot through her as the midwife scowled. Had she said something wrong? She didn't know, she hadn't done this before.

'Let's sit you up.'

She helped her shuffle up and readjusted the pillows behind. Placed the bundle of blankets in her arms.

'We'll start slowly. Get used to him in your arms and I'll gradually pull away from your blankets until he's against your chest.'

It weighed more than she expected, had a warmth of its own. She looked at it. She wasn't sure if she could love it.

'Great, good. Now let's try a feed.'

It squawked.

'See, he likes you. He wants to say hello.'

The midwife pulled the gown back and exposed Tracey's nipple. How was she meant to do this? The midwife nudged its head close to her chest and encouraged her to hold it this way. It wriggled, its beak the wrong shape to latch on.

'That's it, just keep trying. It takes a bit of patience to get it right.'

The midwife held her arm and moved it closer, so it was resting against her breast. Beak opened. It nipped her.

'Ouch, fuck.'

'It's okay, that's okay. It can feel strange the first time.'

The thing wiggled and squeaked. Its pink chin wrinkly like the throat of an old man.

'Try again.'

The midwife nudged its head in her again. It reached forward, latched, its solid beak jittering and vibrating with excitement.

'He's going to pull the whole thing off.'

'It's okay, it may feel like that but it's perfectly natural.'

It felt like needles on her tender breast. She pulled it back. Blood. The midwife grabbed a wet-wipe from the plastic cylinder next to the bed and placed it over the bleeding. She removed the squirming bundle from her arms.

'It gets easier, I promise.'

'I don't want it.'

The midwife folded it back into its coffin, clipped the sides down.

'That's it, little thing, let's give mummy some rest, we can try again later.'

'I don't want it. You can take it the fuck back.'

The coffin was wheeled out.

\*\*\*

It played in the dead leaves outside. She watched it from her make-place near-death bed in her mum's lounge. Her brother, Paul, and her mum were outside with it, not taking their eyes off like it could fly if it wanted to. It was too young to fly. Too young to wean off her breast milk. She'd been trying for three weeks but it still hurt. Its beak grew in strength each day and even the pump reminded her of the abnormality of her baby and she couldn't bring herself to use it no matter how much her brother begged.

She'd watched them change its nappy, feed it bottles, bath it, swaddle it, play with it and cuddle it and still she could see nothing but its black feathers and beady eyes. It was wanting. *Hold it,* they'd say, as though it was something that wanted to be held. *Feed it, it needs you.*

The phone was ringing in the hallway. She felt too heavy to move. The ringing soothed her, like a lullaby from a mechanical mobile hanging above a cot. Her mum turned towards the window, kissed her brother on the head and waded the puddle of fallen leaves out of the garden. One more ring. Her mum's footsteps in the hallway. The handset being removed from the cradle.

'Yes?'

Paul threw some leaves up and watched as they caught the air and floated back down. The thing wiggled and squirmed on the ground beneath him. If only she felt attached to it.

'I told you to stop calling. I don't want her to know you're back,' her mum's hushed voice. Her brothers distant laugh.

'She doesn't want to know.' Her voice deeper now. 'He's well. He's beautiful, couldn't be more perfect. Come on, you know you can't see him.' She could hear her mum's breath from here.

'Listen, if I have anything to do with it, we'll be taking you to court soon. I don't think you want a friendly cup of tea now, do you?'

The click of the phone cradle, her mother's grip loosening. Silence.

The squawk of birds outside. Her brother's distant laughter.

'You're awake?' Her mum leaned against the doorway, body halfway out. 'Hungry?'

She shook her head.

'Paul was talking about taking us out to dinner tonight, if you're up for it. You haven't been out for weeks.'

'He can't afford it.'

'He's your brother, he wants to treat you.'

'Who was on the phone?'

Her mum broke eye contact, looked down.

'It was him, wasn't it? Don't lie to me.'

'He won't hurt you anymore.'

'I don't want you to lie to me mum. I'm not stupid.'

'I'm not lying. Me and Paul are here now, you're safe, you're protected.'

'What the fuck do you know about safe?'

'He's not coming over.'

***

'It's late for you to be up.' Her mum stroked a hand around her back and onto her shoulder, pausing for a moment to inspect the cup of coffee in her hand. Double sugar. She was sitting with the lights off at the kitchen table, watching the tree sway in the wind outside, grey-scale shadows dancing around the window frame.

'I like this time of night. It's peaceful.'

'He went down well tonight. No fights.'

'Tea?'

'Chamomile.'

Her mum stole the warmth of her seat as she stood up.

'I've got a swimming lesson tomorrow, so I'll be out early. Can I take the car?'

'Course you can love.'

'Thanks.'

She refilled the kettle. Clicked the button.

'Mum. He looks strange. He's not what I expected.' Grabbed an empty mug from the cup stand.

'He's premature that's all. He just needs some time to grow and adjust to the world. We're lucky, he's healthy.'

143

'It's not that. He's not right.'
'He couldn't be more beautiful.'
'I don't know what he is.'
'We love him very much.'

\*\*\*

She copied the other mums in the circle, held her baby out, arms trembling.

'This,' she said, 'this is my baby.' She held the crow forwards, wrapped in its baby-pink blanket. The other mums leaned in and cooed. Their own babies bouncing and gurgling up and down in their laps. They all sat cross legged on the floor, bags and buggies in scattered heaps behind each parent. The leader, in a fluorescent pink top with teddy bear ears, clapped her hands together and over-smiled.

'Lovely to meet you. He's beautiful. What's his name?'

He'd grown heavier, almost reaching from her palm to armpit.

'We don't quite have a name yet, do we sweetheart?' Her mum rubbed its head as she spoke. 'But we're thinking Ben, at the moment.'

She fearfully scrutinised the other parent's faces in the circle, feeling their judgement right through to her bones like a cold winter's morning.

'Ben, that's a lovely name,' the leader said, signaling for them all to follow. '*Hello Ben,*' they said in unison.

'And now we sing. As Ben's family are new, why don't we show them our best welcome song, with our smartest smiles. Ready? Arms up, and...'

The song made her cry. She didn't mean to. She didn't see it coming. But once it started it drained out of her like a burst pipe.

\*\*\*

Something woke her suddenly. She found herself gasping for breath, sweat collecting on her face, not dripping but ice cold. Maybe someone was at the window. The blankets wrapped around her legs, her body wedged between the sofa cushions, clothes wet and stuck. She turned her head to look outside, only able to see through the top half of the window, into the night sky, and the hanging branches of the apple tree. Its branches dark and waving, watching her through the smeared glass of the wide Victorian window pane. The old paint on the walls cracking and peeling off in sharp shards, grey rotting wood beneath. An insect crawling along the glass towards the arm of the sofa. She was too tired to squash it.

She'd been dreaming of *him*. His face behind her eyes every time she blinked. It was his face above her, his body on top of her, she was pinned. In her dream she'd wanted to move, to scream, but couldn't. Each time she'd tried, his smile got wider. He was looking into her and there was nothing she could do to look away. She remembered the bruises on her arms, the shape of his fingertips, round and smudged like someone had thrown raspberries and they'd burst on her skin. Her mouth was trembling, she tried to part her lips, teeth gripped. Jaw-sore. It was a dream. It was just a dream. He wasn't here. Mum said she wouldn't let him come. But did they really believe her?

She needed something to stop her shaking. Wine, or gin, or even that cheap-arse lager that her brother liked to drink. She hobbled to the kitchen, feet cold and numb, walking on her heels like a toddler, using the sofa arms, hallway walls and doorway for support. Eyes too sensitive to turn the light on. Just enough moonlight to see the cabinets if she squinted. On her hands and knees, she rummaged through the alcohol cupboard. Things in here from years ago. That banana liquor from the last family holiday to Spain, where they'd gone with Paul and his family, and her then husband. They'd loved him then. Because they thought she did too. They cooed at how he brought her breakfast in bed and treated her to dresses and flaming cocktails. How he'd played with the kids in the pool and shared his bad jokes, happy to be the butt of the joke. How he treated her mum like a queen, telling her she looked nice, opening doors, offering to pay for the family dinners. He was a magician. He knew how to create illusions.

She took the first miniature she could get her hands on and turned the top until the metal teeth snapped. The liquid – sharp on her tongue and her throat – pins and needles in her legs. She took the next and squeezed its plastic sides like a water bottle. Half of it spilling down her front. She took another, and another, barely able to see the labels. A heavy bottle of whiskey, a present maybe, a few Christmases ago? The metal lid as big as a shot glass, but she threw the lid to one side and gulped it down. Pausing to breathe. Wiping her mouth, gasping for air, eyes and face wet. There had to be something more. It wasn't working. Some poison maybe, the bleach, there was bleach under the sink. Anything to burn the pain away. Because how could someone like her live with something like this? She gulped the last of the whiskey, barely wincing at the burn now, and scrambled over the discarded bottles and broken glass to the sink, hands too trembling to grip the cabinet door, shaking it open then closed again in her rush, in her panic, in the chaos of her out-of-control thought. Her body not her own. It was only the third time he said it that she heard her brother.

Paul leant against the kitchen door and for a moment he looked like *him*, the shape of his outline, broad silhouette, hands poised ready for a fight.

'Marc?' Her voice shallow, fear gripping her lungs stopped them from filling, breath trapped in her throat.

'What are you doing?' he said.

The figure stepped forward, the moonlight shifted, apple tree branches dancing on his face. He looked like a watercolour painting.

'Paul?'

'What's going on?'

The fear that shot through her subsided as her brother took a step closer. A friendly face. It might be angry, but it was a face she knew, a face that hadn't hurt her before.

'You've been drinking?'

He knelt down next to her, inspected the empty bottles and strewn bottle tops surrounding her, like a salt circle at a séance. He touched her arm: ice cold, clammy. She could feel how wide her eyes were looking at him but she couldn't make her heart calm.

'Get up,' he wrapped an arm under hers and tried to lift. Her legs wouldn't obey. 'Come on, get up', he said as he tried again. Another try. Defeated, he sat down next to her, shoving the guilty mess aside, his back against the cabinet. The fridge hummed loudly.

'It sucks, I know. But you have to think of Ben.'

She said nothing, her tongue puffy in her mouth. He took her hand.

'Drinking's not the answer.'

She tried to talk, tried to explain herself, but her lips were clumsy, tiny clunks and breaths escaping her mouth with no real words.

'Coffee,' he said, standing up and switching the kettle on.

The cold patio air on her face reminded her of how drunk she was. She hadn't been this drunk this quickly since secondary school. He held the warm mug to her face and encouraged her to blow and sip gently. The soft hum of the night air surrounded them.

'I'm sorry sis, but I have to ask, are things really that bad?'

They watched the lights of a plane passing overhead, drifting into the pollution bubble above the city and eventually moving out of sight behind the trees at the end of the garden.

'It was worse than you think,' she took a gulp, suddenly stone cold-sober.

'What do you mean?'

'He did more than just shout at me and bully me. It was hell.'

'But you were good once. I never saw you argue.'

'He's clever like that.'

'What do you mean?'

'Forget it. It was tough, that's all.'

He put his cup down and grabbed her hand.

'I know it's been tough. But this isn't the way to handle it. You need to pull yourself together.'

'Fuck you, Paul.'

They both looked up, nothing moving or happening up there to drag their attention away. She shivered.

'I'm sorry,' he took his coat off, wrapped it around her. Inside, the spare room light came on, their mum doing the night feed. They looked up for a moment, sobering light flooding the patio, too hesitant to look at each other's faces and the state they were in. She remembered she had no slippers no. 'I knew you had a rough relationship, but I just assumed you were happy, you know, because of Ben.'

'My baby wasn't planned.'

'Well, I assumed so.'

'No. I mean, it wasn't my choice.'

Their mum singing gently in the room, the chord of the lullaby machine being pulled. Twinkle Twinkle Little Star. A comet passing overhead.

He leaned his shoulder against hers.

\*\*\*

It hopped around at the front of the trolley, wrapped up inside its baby pink blanket. Curious at the metal of the trolley bars rather than the tins of food and plastic packaging slowly being added. The woman next to her, Delia, the community midwife, at least she thought that's what her name was, or had it been Davina, taking her down the aisles like a tour guide, full of advice and lists. Davina wore a blue pinny with white stripes and ill-fitting jeans. Sensible shoes. Her hands were constantly gesturing.

'It's nearly time to wean him. You need to think about what sort of solid food you want to try him on. Think about soft vegetables and nutritious food. Nothing too spicy or too strong flavoured.'

She walked as fast as she was talking, pointing with her pen toward foods to consider, a double tap for the good offers and cheap prices.

'It's not about what food you want to eat. He'll be sensitive to things. His taste buds will be changing. He may love something one day and hate it the next.'

Like a good mother, she obeyed, took a bottle of something off the shelf and placed it next to her crow baby, its curious squawk as it looked up at her.

A couple pushed a baby in a trolley next to them, full of military action list-ticking and ingredient gathering, baby snacking on a packet of organic something or other in the trolley seat, legs a playful swing. Roll-calling each item as it left the shelf and entered the trolley. No hesitance. No delay. They barely noticed her, other than to move around her and get to the items they needed. They seemed well-coordinated and completely in control of parenthood. The opposite of her.

Why did she not feel like that?

'You have to think about what you want your baby to be,' Davina continued. 'Some parents don't think about this. They feed their kids crisps and sugar, fatty foods and then they're surprised when their kids don't grow up to be athletes. If you want them to be athletes you've got to feed them like an athlete. If you want them to be scientists or psychologists then you have to feed them brain food, mackerel and spinach, all the greens.'

Davina pointed at another tin and tapped the price. She obeyed and put it in the trolley. They walked in time, stopping every few steps to fill the trolley with something new. In perfect unison and routine. There was only fifteen minutes before Davina had to see her next client.

She pushed her baby around the corner, trolley almost full. Healthy. She wanted it to be healthy.

\*\*\*

A quiet cup of tea. She'd forgotten how good it could taste. The kitchen table to herself, clutter free, a clean body, some perfume on. Blue sky outside.

They both entered at the same time, noise filled the space from the floor to the ceiling. She put her fingers in her ears. They were shouting. Moving circles around her.

Paul's voice: 'I don't understand, he's not taking the bottle.'

'Maybe he's not hungry,' her mum was out of breath.

'He's crying.'

'He could just be cold. Or too warm. Take his jumper off.'

'That's his hungry cry.'

She hummed, the sound too intense, the phone being picked up, the beep of numbers. They knocked house keys off the side and chinked discarded glasses together. The creak of the floorboards and the cabinet doors opening and closing. It was like someone had turned the TV up to maximum volume and she couldn't find the mute button.

'You could ring the nurse,' Mum said.

'I'll try ringing the nurse. Take him,' said her brother.

'I'll take him.'

'Try taking him to the nursery. See if you can distract him.'

'I'll try and distract him. You call the nurse.'

They left the room. Taking the noise with them. As she exhaled, she realised she'd been holding her breath.

Later, a quiet moment. They'd left her alone with him in her arms. The TV set to a kids programme though he was still too little to understand. She munched slowly on toast, not feeling hungry but obeying orders to eat. She hummed, the background noise of the TV mummering and the lawn mower in the distance a nice distraction. It shifted in her arms. Warmth calming and nurturing to her. Looked up at her with its cute beady eyes and yellow beak. Chattering the edges together slightly.

Perhaps, it was hungry?

Perhaps, it wanted some of her love?

She took a bite of toast, moved it carefully around her mouth, crushing the crust and the insides with saliva until it was one small ball of mush, warm and easy to digest. She moved it closer to her mouth, held the mush between her teeth and hovered it over its beak. Moved her face from side to side, tempting it. Eat, baby. Eat the food. It shivered in its blanket below her.

\*\*\*

Bare feet, from smooth tiles, to brick, to warm grass. A soft blow of warm wind against her legs. She walked slowly into the garden. Air felt cool, through her nostrils, down her throat, filling her lungs. Muscles in her shoulders letting go. Her body drifting, carrying itself across the lawn. She didn't have to think how to move. A phone rang in the kitchen. Only two rings. Her mum answered. She stopped moving. Hung her head back, up at the sky. Watched the clouds moving swiftly overhead, seeing shapes and figures, like it was a painting, like it was a puddle of water dripping with colour, someone's finger swirling it, playful and enticing. It was peaceful, like nothing she'd ever seen. Her breath fresh and new. Mum's footsteps behind her, creak of the patio step.

'I can't believe it. Marc's agreed to the divorce.'

Behind her, a baby's wail. It reminded her of the babies in the parent's group, or the post-natal classes she'd been to. The gasping, squeezing cry of an overwhelmed little human, unable to use anything to express itself other than its surprisingly strong lungs.

Paul's whisper, his tone high and shifting: 'Hush, it's okay Ben. You hungry? You want some food?'

She turned slowly. Moment by moment. The sun lighting the fence and casting shadows on their lawn, the tray of drinks and apple cores from earlier on the grass, cheap metal plastic of the tray reflecting the sun, shining into her eyes. She squinted, a pool of cold black tea beneath the arm of the tea pot, the sound of the neighbours lawnmower, the neighbour's head bopping up and down over the fence as they bent to collect weeds, softly humming to themselves. The radio was talking in the kitchen – two hosts laughing and over excited – an introduction to a strangely familiar song. She noticed the back of Paul's head, balding and combed over. The blue of his jumper and the white collar sticking up on one side, the backs of the soles of his shoes, thick rubber treads. His knees on the floor, leaves combed to the side. A baby mat, soft pink, blue and yellow by the roots of the tree which was lumpy from the grass and sticks. In front of him, a plastic toy, disgruntled and at an angle, dropped by a fickle hand. The cold of her mum's fingers newly placed on her arm made her flinch. She watched the sway of the skinny trees at the end of the garden, the cat prowling their fence, jumping down out of sight. And Paul's arms around something small and soft, wiggling. A tiny head of hair and a tiny red face over his shoulder, wailing, eyes scrunched and pink toothless gums. A tiny human hand balled into a fist. Eyes so tight it couldn't see the world. Hands so little they couldn't lift a thing. Pink mouth, open and angry.

Her mum's voice in her ear: 'We'll fight this together, baby.'

And her brother turning, a baby in arms, gentle look on his face, 'Get the bottle mum, he needs a feed.'

MARIA DONOVAN

# Aftermath

In the game Statue of Liberty, the one with the strongest arm wins. 'It's not fair!' whines Half-sister, dropping her hand.

Janna takes the prize: her first trip with Father to Market. 'You can do my work tomorrow,' she says, smiling and sidestepping Half-sister's kick.

Half-mother has sewn a new yellow tunic for Janna with a bee on the pocket, a reminder of her real mother. Father says she ran after a honeybee and was lost. Soon after that he brought home Half-mother, ripe in a red dress like a tomato that must burst. She had a dowry of fine sable brushes, perfect for stroking blossoms with pollen.

Janna climbed the apple trees and they brought forth fruit. Half-mother brought forth Half-sister and Father said, 'Another girl.'

Now Half-mother is swelling again. She can't walk far.

After mowing, the grass hasn't grown; the steel sky lets down no rain. Janna and Father drive their thin sheep along the dyke above the drowned land, pushing against a hot wind blowing towards home. The roofs of houses are red hats floating on salt water.

At Market, half-empty stalls shake in the wind; one collapses with a crash of old glass.

The sheep are sold before Father shoves Janna into the pen. 'Take the brush,' he says. 'Statue of Liberty!' Bewildered, Janna raises her hand.

Father turns away, shouting, 'What will you pay for this girl? A well-trained pollinator!'

Janna closes her eyes, arm trembling as the first fat drops begin to fall.

MIKE KILGANNON

# The Hercules Reopened

It was only the third but by some distance the biggest penis Joyce had ever seen. Within the hour she'd see a clutch more in various states of readiness, in the flesh. This one was brandished at her from a poster for a film – loosely based, as far as she could tell, on *Ben Hur*. She stood, transfixed by the sheer monstrousness of it, reminded, ridiculously, of the tyrannosaurus rex poster that was still above the desk in Anthony's room. A desk still groaning with A-level revision notes, textbooks, pencil shavings, two mugs long since mould-blackened – a desk with a still-locked drawer, in which she knew, now, had always known, there'd be magazines from which more of these appendages would burst forth like fleshy pop-up books.

The bomb had been hidden in a drawer, too, of a vending machine – not the sort they'd had to start installing in these sorts of places since boys started getting iller and iller – but one that sold chocolate bars, fizzy pop, breath mints. Replaced now with shelving for spare towels. Beautifully clean.

She'd had to see this place for herself.

When she'd given her name they'd remembered Anthony's and let her in – led her down the narrow stairs, into the damp heat of this place with the smell of bleach, let her stand and stay a while in the place her boy, her gentle boy, had bunked off double geography and caught his last two buses to get to.

AMANDA O'CALLAGHAN

# Vigil

Far from here, in rooms of glass and steel, they know. That the bones in the mud are a dog, not a boy. That a rind of metal, small as your ear, pulled a plane from the sky. That a widget's fin the size of your fist sank a ship, rolled a train. That a single seed in a skelter of leaves finds the place, nails the man. Under points of light, latex fingers worry the tiny, fractured pieces, lift the scraps of lives.

And I will wait here, watching the seasons, holding this shirt in practiced hands, soft on my face, the scent of you long gone. I will wait here until they say, 'This. This is your boy.'

DANIEL BENNETT

# Ligature

It's about 10am. I am thirty-five years old and up a scaffold with my dad in the rain. We are scraping loose paint off the front of some house. I am damp and cold, and sober. But it's not so bad. He wears a floppy decorator's hat, I wear a white baseball cap. The woman whose house it is bought her fridge/freezer for £8000 the cleaning lady said. My father scrapes vigorously away, complaining about his lot: His life is all hard-work and worry and he never found the time to stay being an artist. He is 62 with a bad back and his knees are going. I'm looking at the tufts of hair on the back of his neck and I want to smooth them down. I don't want him to talk anymore – it's making me uncomfortable. Like I should hug him or something and I'm not doing that. At least not up here. I look over the edge and imagine myself slipping and falling; seeing myself smashed on the wet paving below. Seeing my dad slip, I know exactly how his face would be: rigid, with eyes bulging as if enraged; rage rapidly dissolving into to dismay. I see him falling but I don't see him smashing on the ground. Falling in his overalls, dismay on his face. I just see him falling. My dad. Maybe I see him smash too, maybe I lied about that. I love my father, but I cannot catch him.

LOUISE CATO

# Small Bones

The beetroots bleed deep into the seams of her fingers. She doesn't notice the red beads forming fat as they roll slow over crease and knuckle, tapping shocks onto the white porcelain below. Their root stumps are the open wounds of removed limbs. Sinew and tissue. I sweep the quiet, discarded leaves from the sideboard beside her, slipping back unseen to watch the pink bloom on my palms.

Each year I can't look away, and later, I'll dream in dark velvet. Of plunging my thumb deep into the hole left by a loud gunshot. A belly knife flashing as it slices through pig skin; white rind and stiff pale hairs slammed prickling onto a heavy cold slab.

She won't say a word until they are packed into jars for winter. The same heavy shuffle, she stoops to lift the iron latch of the oven, her back always to me, taking the heat for herself. I have red stains on my white apron and I watch her reflection in the glass as she moves.

In the mornings, I check the traps and find warm mice, sometimes slick, oily rats inside. I like the weight of them, their bones smooth-shifting as I squeeze. One day I'll leave one, silent, on the butcher's marble for her to find.

ISABELLA MEAD

# Genocide Memorial Week, Rwanda 2019

I stayed in all week. The hut was pervaded with a strange new quietness: a silence stippled with tiny teeth loosening the mud walls by fracturing the whitewash and steadily upturning the earth underneath. A silence infiltrated with insidious clicking and drilling and sucking, like a kind of ruptured tinnitus.

Termites. I couldn't face dealing with them; I didn't want to touch them. Besides, I didn't know where to buy a new pot of whitewash; I'd only been volunteering two months. I didn't know the Kinyarwanda word for 'whitewash.' And it seemed disrespectful to ask my neighbours for advice with such a trivial problem.

So, gently, the termites became entrenched. Their projects bloomed. And I watched.

One night, Baptiste stopped by on his way to a memorial ceremony. 'You will join us?' he asked cordially.

'I – maybe.' I said. He knew I would not. It's not my history, I thought; the West turned its back in 1994; I shouldn't go, out of respect.

So I stayed in. That night, I caught drifts of the ceremony down in the valley: desultory microphones rigged up and holding out even in rain, magnifying the ceaseless reciting of names. And names and names, and now more names.

The next day I ventured out for a walk. I didn't lock the door – no one did. I returned to find my walls newly whitewashed.

'You had an urgent problem,' Baptiste said. 'We came while you were out.'

I did not say thank you, out of respect.

# Biographies

## Judges

**Kirsty Logan**'s latest book is *The Gloaming*; she is the author of three short story collections, two novels, a flash fiction chapbook, and a short memoir. Her collaborative work includes 'Lord Fox', a show of spoken word, song and harp music with Kirsty Law and Esther Swift; and 'The Knife-Thrower's Wife', an Angela Carter-inspired album with Kathryn Williams and Polly Paulusma. Her books have won the Lambda Literary Award, Polari Prize, Saboteur Award, Scott Prize and Gavin Wallace Fellowship. Her work has been adapted for stage, recorded for radio and podcasts, exhibited in galleries and distributed from a vintage Wurlitzer cigarette machine.

**Hollie McNish** is a full time writer who loves writing poetry. She has published three poetry collections *Papers*, *Cherry Pie* and *Plum*, and one poetic memoir on politics and parenthood, *Nobody Told Me*, of which the Scotsman suggested 'The world needs this book' and for which she won the Ted Hughes Award. In 2017 *Nobody Told Me* was translated into German, French and Spanish and released in the USA. In 2016 she co-wrote a play *Offside* with Sabrina Mahfouz, relating the two hundred year history of UK women's football.

She has written a few select commissions including subjects such as: orgasm inequality for Durex; various for The Economist Education Foundation and most recently 'War Whores' – a history of sex work in World War One for the 14-18 / Roundhouse LDN partnership.

Hollie tours continuously all over the UK, Europe and beyond and is a big fan of freely accessible online readings – her poetry videos have attracted millions of views worldwide. She is currently working on a new collection of poems and stories.

**Daniel Bennett** was born in London. He is primarily a visual-artist, painting under the name of 'Daniel Roch', and writes mostly for himself. He has had a somewhat patchwork-life, living in Ireland, New York, and Brighton, and been in all kinds of jobs, from general-labouring, to the creation of theatrical-sets and sculpture. He currently lives in East-London, helping look after his elderly parents and working as a freelance Art-Handler/Gallery-Technician. He commutes between these stints to Central Portugal, where he helps his partner set up her small-holding/farm.

**Alison Binney** teaches English in a secondary school and on the PGCE course at the University of Cambridge. She has recently been published in *The North*, *Magma*, *Under the Radar*, *The Fenland Reed* and *Impossible Archetype*. Two of her poems currently appear on buses in Guernsey, and she has a poem forthcoming in a Smith/Doorstop anthology of poems about running.

**Joshua Blackman** graduated from the University of Sussex in 2016 with an MA in Modern and Contemporary Literature. He lives in Bognor Regis and, when not writing poetry, works in an art gallery bookshop in Chichester.

**Joseph Allen Boone** is the author of three works of non-fiction (*The Homoerotics of Orientalism* being the latest); the libretto for *CON-MAN*, a musical 'apocalypse' based on Herman Melville's *The Confidence-Man*; and eight short stories. He has recently completed a novel, *Furnace Creek*, which is circulating among agents. Last year *Furnace Creek* was the only adult novel among seven finalists for the Leapfrog Press Fiction award, and this year it was one of three 'highly commended' finalists (and only novel) in the multi-genre Beverly Prize competition. His stories have been finalists in the Hackney Literary Awards story competition (third prize), the F(r)iction Magazine Short Story Contest (top three), the New South Writing Contest, and the Rick DeMarinis Short Story contest. These and other stories are currently being gathered in a manuscript titled *Precocity*. Boone is the recipient of writing fellowships from the Guggenheim Foundation, ACLS, the Huntington Library, the National Humanities Center, and the Stanford Humanities Center and residencies at Bellagio, Bogliasco, and Valaraiso.

**Penny Boxall** won the 2016 Edwin Morgan Poetry Award, the 2018 Mslexia/PBS Poetry Competition and a 2019 Northern Writers' Award.

She was shortlisted for the 2019 Alpine Fellowship. She has held residencies at Gladstone's Library, Hawthornden Castle and Chateau de Lavigny. In autumn 2019 she is Visiting Research Fellow in the Creative Arts at Merton College, Oxford.

**Louise Cato** finally started writing last year. She comes from Buckinghamshire, but now divides her time between Somerset and Bristol where she works for a democracy company making online tools to bring citizens closer to decisions which affect them, which isn't so easy in the current climate. *Small Bones* is her first published story.

**Mikaella Clements** is an Australian writer currently based in Berlin. Her fiction has been published in *Hazlitt*, *Catapult*, *Overland Literary Journal* and more, and her non-fiction has been published widely. She was shortlisted for the Galley Beggar Prize 2019, and her fiction has been anthologised in Black Inc.'s *Best Summer Stories* and *Kill Your Darlings' New Australian Fiction*. Her first novel *The View Was Exhausting*, which she co-wrote with her wife Onjuli Datta is due out in summer 2021, via Headline in the UK and Commonwealth and Grand Central in the US.

**Maria Donovan** enjoys learning languages and writing fiction. Her debut novel, *The Chicken Soup Murder*, was a finalist for the Dundee International Book Prize and runner-up in the Dorchester Literature Festival Writing Prize 2019. Maria grew up in Bridport before moving to the Netherlands, where she trained as a nurse. She travelled around Europe as a musician and performer, studied English at the University of Glamorgan, and worked as a teacher there, becoming a Senior Lecturer in Creative Writing. She now lives back home in Bridport and is writing full time: mainly flash fiction, short stories and her second novel.

**Marie-Louise Eyres** was briefly an actor then she worked for several years in London literary agencies and at the BBC, where she negotiated deals for writers and performers. She has spent the past decade in the USA, living in Los Angeles and Washington DC with her favourite husband, Alan and their children. Her poems have featured in various print and online journals including *Smiths Knoll*, *Obsessed with Pipework*, *Iota*, *Rain Dog*, *The Coffee House*, *Fragments*, *Ink, Sweat & Tears*, *The Write Launch*, *Algebra of Owls*, *Cathexis Northwest Press*.

**Mark Farley** was raised in Africa – a childhood spent running wild and barefoot in sunny scrubland, during which he survived two dog maulings, a swarm of killer bees and being run over by a horse. His published work includes: 'Flying Ants', *Flash: The International Short-Short Story Magazine*; 'Hugs are more important than potatoes', Amaryllis Poetry; 'The Walrus, the Carpenter and the Grubbertun', Spilling Cocoa Over Martin Amis; 'Sync' and 'Floating', The Casket of Fictional Delights; 'Earlier Than Camels', Domestic Cherry; 'You will remember Vienna', *The Literary Hatchet*; and 'Grans & Ammo', *Sanitarium Horror Magazine* (a factual account of mad old ladies fighting zombies). Say hi to Mark on twitter (@mumbletoes) or via his website (mumbletoes.co.uk).

**Mark Fiddes** is a previous runner-up in The Bridport Prize (2015). He has published two books of poetry (*The Rainbow Factory* and *The Chelsea Flower Show Massacre*) both with Templar Publishing. He was placed third this year in the National Poetry Competition and has won the Ruskin Prize among many other international awards. His work has recently appeared in *Poetry Review*, *The Irish Times*, *Poem Magazine*, *Magma* and *The New European*. He's currently Brexiled in the Middle East.

**Jane Flett** is a Scottish writer living in Berlin. Her work has been commissioned for BBC Radio 4, anthologised in the *Best British Poetry*, and awarded the Scottish Book Trust New Writer Award. She's been published in over 70 literary journals and translated into Polish, Croatian and Japanese. Jane is also a recipient of the New Orleans Writing Residency and one half of the riot-grrrl band Razor Cunts. http://janeflett.com/

**Ross Foster** is a writer from Tamworth with a love of speculative fiction. He holds a BA in English with Creative Writing (1st class Hons) and works at Birmingham City University creating multimedia content for research marketing. Always ready to experiment with different forms, he is now dabbling in writing and recording his first fiction podcast and creating stories using social media and web platforms.

**Sulaxana Hippisley** has taught A-level English for the last eleven years and currently teaches in a Sixth form college in North London. Her short stories have been long listed by the Bristol Short Story Prize, Desi Writers Lounge and Chawton House's Jane Austen Short Story Award. In 2014, she was awarded runner up in the Asian Writer Short Story competition for her story 'On being Mary.' In 2017, she was selected to be part of the Almasi League, a writer development programme run under the tutelage of Courttia Newland and the Arts Council. More recently, her memoir 'This is the house my father built' was shortlisted for the 2019 Spread the Word Life Writing Prize. She is currently working on a novel set in Sri Lanka and lives in North West London with her four year old daughter.

**Jenny Karlsson** lives in her native Swedish Lappland where she is editing her short stories and working odd jobs. She holds a Creative Writing MA from the University of East Anglia and her work has appeared in *The White Review*.

**Mike Kilgannon** is an English teacher and dad living in Sheffield. He grew up in St Helens, Merseyside and has been scribbling in secret ever since. 'The Hercules Reopened' is his first published piece of flash fiction.

**Jimmy Lowther** comes from Durham originally but has lived in Wiltshire since 1991. He recently retired from a career in the NHS. Before entering the nursing profession he had been a tractor driver, a binman and a soldier. He studied English at Bath Spa University College and completed a MA at Manchester University. He has previously published poetry in *Envoi*, *Reach*, and *The Journal*.

**Jim McElroy** is a new voice first published in 2018. His work led to his selection by Poetry Ireland as one of Ireland's emerging poets – for their Introductions Series 2019. He has read at the International Literature Festival Dublin, the Hillsborough Literary Festival and the Crescent Arts Centre, Belfast. His poetry has been published in the *Cap Arts New Writer's Anthology* in both 2018 and 2019 and in *The Honest Ulsterman*. He is an honours graduate of Queen's University, Belfast (Business) and a member of the Institute Of Directors. His poetry muses over the first and second age, stares into the third; he is working towards his first collection.

**Isabella Mead** is Head of Learning at The Story Museum in Oxford, through which she leads the teaching of the art of storytelling and creative writing. She previously worked as Learning Manager the Roald Dahl Museum and Story Centre and as a secondary English teacher in London. From 2010 to 2012 she spent 2 years in a rural Rwandan village training teachers through VSO. Her poems have been longlisted for the National Poetry Competition (2017), Highly Commended in the Bridport Prize (2016), the Cafe Writers Prize (2018) and the Mslexia Pamphlet Competition (2017). This is her first piece of fiction.

**Anna Metcalfe**'s first book of short stories, *Blind Water Pass*, was published by John Murray in 2016. Her work has appeared in *The Best British Short Stories*, *The Dublin Review*, *Lighthouse Journal*, *The Warwick Review* and *The Lonely Crowd*, among other places, and has previously been shortlisted for the Sunday Times Short Story Award. She lives in Birmingham, where she teaches Creative Writing.

**Alissa Jones Nelson** grew up in Southern California and has since travelled widely and lived in Spain, the Czech Republic, Japan, Scotland, and Germany. Her first novel was shortlisted for the Dundee International Book Prize, and her short story 'Elsewhere, OK' was a runner-up for the 2017 Berlin Writing Prize. She was a finalist for the 2019 Curt Johnson Prose Award in Fiction and the 2019 Craft Short Fiction Prize. Her short stories have appeared in the anthologies *Home Is Elsewhere* and *27 Stories*. She holds a PhD from the Centre for the Study of Religion and Politics at the University of St. Andrews. She lives in Berlin, where she earns her living as an editor and translator.

**Amanda O'Callaghan** is a Brisbane-based author whose short stories and flash fiction have been published and won awards in Australia, the United Kingdom and Ireland. Her work has been awarded and shortlisted in the Bath Flash Fiction Award, Flash 500, Bristol Short Story Prize, Aeon Award, Fish Short Story Prize and others. A former advertising executive, Amanda holds English degrees from King's College London, and a PhD from the University of Queensland. Her debut collection, *This Taste for Silence*, was published by the University of Queensland Press (UQP) in June 2019. It has just been shortlisted for the Readings Prize for New Australian Fiction. www.amandaocallaghan.com

**Lani O'Hanlon** is the author of *Dancing the Rainbow* (Mercier Press) and a Poetry Chapbook *The Little Theatre* (Artlinks) and facilitates creative writing, movement and dance with Waterford Healing Arts Trust. She has an MA in creative writing from Lancaster University and has studied fiction with The Stinging Fly. She received a travel and training award in 2017 from the National Arts Council to complete a first novel set in Ireland and Greece.

Her work has been published in *POETRY (Chicago)*, *Poetry Ireland Review*, *Mslexia*, *The Irish Times*, *Southword*, *The Stinging Fly*, *ORBIS*, *Poethead*, *The Moth*, *Skylight Poets*, *Solas Nua*, *Phenomenal Literature*, *Verbal Art* in the Anthologies; *Small Lives*, *Poddle*, *Halleluiah for 50ft Women*, *Bloodaxe*, *Ten Poems for Breakfast*, Candlestick Press, *The Lea*

*Green Down*, Fiery Arrow *2018*, *Magnum Opus*, The Authors Press and regularly broadcast on RTE Irish national radio; shortlisted for The Bridport Prize, FISH, Mslexia, DiBiase, HC Poetry on the Lake, and a prizewinner Hennessey New Irish Writing, Dromineer, The Irish Writer's Centre – Novel Fair, Brewery Lane, William Allingham, Over the Edge and Hungry Hill's Poets meet Politics. A poetry film with Director Fiona Aryan, Going to the Well, was shortlisted for O Bhéal International Poetry Film competition in 2018.

**Hesse Phillips** is an alumna of GrubStreet Boston's Novel Incubator Program and currently has a novel in progress. She also holds a PhD in Drama, specializing in Elizabethan theatre. Born and raised in a small town in Pennsylvania, she now lives in Madrid, Spain with her wife.

**Sharon Phillips** started learning to write poems a few years ago, after she retired from her post as Principal of King Edward VI College, Stourbridge. Her poems have been published online and in print, and have been shortlisted for the Bridport Prize (2017), the Indigo Firsts pamphlet competition (2018) and the WoLF Poetry Competition (2019). Sharon won the Borderlines Poetry Competition in 2017 and was among the winners of the Poetry Society Members' Competition in November 2018. She has recently moved to Otley, in West Yorkshire.

**Dominic Price** graduated from college with a 2:1 (Hons) Degree in English & History. Since then, he has spent short periods of time in work and long periods of time out of work. He is indebted to his parents, with whom he lives, to his friends, for their support, and to the State, for its largesse. He currently volunteers for one of the UK's largest charities and continues to write in his spare time.

**Gemma Reeves** is a writer and teacher who lives and works in London. She graduated with distinction from the MA in Creative Writing at Bath Spa University, and holds an MA in Twentieth Century Literature from Goldsmiths. She has co-written award-winning non-fiction books and children's storybooks. In 2017, she was shortlisted for the V.S. Pritchett Short Story Prize. She has recently completed her first novel Victoria Park, represented by Seren Adams at United Agents.

**Stephen Spratt** is a researcher and writer who was born and brought up in Oxfordshire. He lived for many years in Brighton, undertaking research and teaching at the Institute of Development Studies, and slowly developing what has become a deep interest in poetry. He has been longlisted for the UK National Poetry Competition and published in Poetry Ireland Review, and now lives in West Cork in Ireland where he tries to balance work and family life, while also writing the odd poem.

**Kenneth Steven** is a widely published poet, novelist and children's author. Sixteen of his poetry collections have appeared to date, and he has written and presented many poetry-related programmes for BBC Radio. His best-known collections are *Iona*, *A Song Among The Stones* and *West*. He is published by Saint Andrew Press, Wild Goose Publications and SPCK and his work can be seen at his website https://kennethsteven.co.uk/

**Amy Stewart** is a freelance copywriter by day, writer of woman-centric speculative fiction by night. She has a degree in English Language and Literature from Newcastle University, and has recently completed an MA in Creative Writing at York St John University. Originally from Edinburgh, she now lives in York with her partner, Phil.

**Nici West** is the co-founder and editor of Boudica Press and a freelance copywriter and editor. Her stories have been published in *Dark Ink Press*, *Dark Lane Books*, *Weave Magazine*, *Nib Magazine*, *Dead Ink* and she was shortlisted for the Flash Mob Writing Competition at Chorlton Arts Festival. Her short story 'Donor' was shortlisted for the Willesden Herald Short Story Prize.

**Fathima Zahra** is an Indian poet based in Essex. Her work has been featured across BBC World News, The New Indian Express and Young Poets Network. She is a Roundhouse Poetry Collective alumni and a runner up in the Roundhouse Poetry Slam final 2018. In her writing, she explores the lives of the diaspora, identity and belonging. She has been long listed for the Out-Spoken Poetry Prize 2019 and the Women Poet's Prize 2018 (Rebecca Swift Foundation). Her debut pamphlet *Datepalm Ghazals* comes out with Burning Eye Books in 2020.